THE
AMAZING
COLLECTION™

D1368224

THE
POST-EXILIC
BOOKS

SET 3

:bioq

bioq

The Hiding Place
book by Corh ____

The Husband's secret
? book
"Dream Big"
Henrietta Meers

THE AMAZING COLLECTION™

THE POST-EXILIC BOOKS

1 CHRONICLES, 2 CHRONICLES,
EZRA, NEHEMIAH, AND ESTHER

SET 3

BIG DREAM
MINISTRIES

No part of *The Amazing Collection*, whether audio, video, or print, may be reproduced in any form without written permission from Big Dream Ministries, Inc., P.O. Box 324, 12460 Crabapple Road, Suite 202, Alpharetta, Georgia 30004.
1-678-366-3460
www.theamazingcollection.org

ISBN-13 : 978-1-932199-03-1
ISBN-10 : 1-932199-03-9

Cover design by Brand Navigation and Arvid Wallen
Cover composite image by Getty Images and Corbis
Creative Team: Leigh McLeroy, Kathy Mosier, Pat Reinheimer, Glynese Northam

Some of the anecdotal illustrations in this book are true to life and are included with the permission of the persons involved. All other illustrations are composites of real situations, and any resemblance to people living or dead is coincidental.

Unless otherwise identified, all Scripture quotations in this publication are taken from the *New American Standard Bible* (NASB), © The Lockman Foundation 1960, 1962, 1963, 1968, 1971, 1972, 1973, 1975, 1977, 1995.

Printed in the United States.

7 8 9 10 / 13

Welcome to
The Amazing Collection
The Bible, Book by Book

It is amazing how a love letter arriving at just the right time can gladden the heart, refresh the soul, and restore the passion of the beloved. When lovers are separated by distance and can communicate only through the written word, that word becomes the lifeline of their love.

The greatest love letter ever written often sits on our shelves unopened as we go about our lives, sometimes fearful, burdened, anxious, in pain, and in doubt, not knowing that on its pages we can find all we need to live the life we have always wanted.

In this love letter we will discover God, and through Him we will receive hope, assurance, freedom from fear, guidance for everyday life, wisdom, joy, peace, power, and above all, the way to salvation. We will find the life we have always longed for — *abundant* life.

The Bible is simply a love letter compiled into sixty-six books and written over a period of sixteen hundred years by more than forty authors living on three continents. Although the authors came from different backgrounds, there is one message, one theme, one thread that runs throughout the entire Bible from the first book, Genesis, to the last book, Revelation. That message is God's redeeming love for mankind — a message that is as relevant for us today as it was two thousand years ago.

God has written the Bible so that men and women might enter into an intimate relationship with Him and see His character, His works, His power, and His love. It would be tragic to read these books and never come to know your God! Therefore, as you go through this study, listen to the lectures, read the Scripture, and do your daily homework. Make it your heart's desire to know God intimately. Read each page of the Bible as if it were a love letter written by the hand of God to you personally. Bask in His great love, stand in awe of His mighty power, bow before His majesty, and give thanksgiving and adoration to the One who is all-present, all-knowing, all-merciful, and all-loving. He is on every page, and He is speaking to you.

The Bible is a book inspired by God Himself. It is His story, His love letter, His invitation to you to become His child through His Son, Jesus Christ. It is the Word of God . . . indeed, the most Amazing Collection.

CONTENTS

ESTHER

MAPS, CHARTS, AND DIAGRAMS

WORKBOOK GUIDE

The Amazing Collection is a study of the Bible, book by book This third study includes the five books of the Bible we have titled The Post-Exilic Books. The following will acquaint you with the design of this series.

The entire Bible will be studied one book at a time through a teaching video and a written study. The teaching video includes music to stir the heart, graphics to enlighten the mind, and a personal testimony to bring the theme of that particular book to life.

The workbook contains:

1. An introduction to summarize each book.

2. Outlines to be used while watching each of the teaching videos. The answers to the outline blanks are given during the videos and can also be found in the key at the back of your workbook.

3. *Learning for Life* discussion questions to be used after viewing the videos. (If your group is large, we recommend forming small discussion groups.)

4. Five daily lessons of homework for each book.

5. A memory verse for each book.

6. Various maps, charts, and diagrams.

7. A review at the end of each book to refresh your memory. The answers to the review are found in the *Review It!* sections in the margins at the end of the lessons for Day One through Day Four. The fifth review question is a review of the memory verse.

Before you begin the homework, ask God to show you how to apply the truths of Scripture to your own life. At the beginning of each day's lesson in the workbook, there are two choices for the daily reading. The *Complete Read* enables you to read the entire book over the course of that study. During busy times, the *Quick Read* allows you to read a few key chapters or verses from that book. The daily lesson will require a small amount of time each day to complete. Of course, feel free to extend that time with additional study.

One of the incredible things about the Word of God is that you can read the same Scripture at different times in your life and gain new insights with each reading. God's Word is inexhaustible, and it is living; it has the power to produce life-changing results.

Our prayer for you as you begin your journey through *The Amazing Collection* is that you will learn for life the purpose, main characters, geography, and time period of every book in the Bible. But above all, we pray that you will come to know more intimately the God of the Bible, His Son Jesus Christ, and the Holy Spirit.

The Post-Exilic Books at a Glance

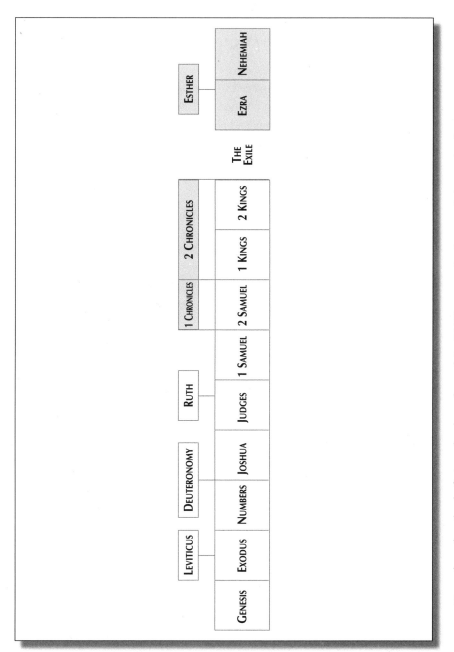

To see how these books fit into the chronology of the Old Testament books as a whole, see the chart on page 145.

OVERVIEW OF THE POST-EXILIC BOOKS

The following pages provide an overview of each of the books you will be studying in this set. They are designed to be cut out and used as quick reference cards with the main facts of the book on the front and the memory verse on the back.

You might find it helpful to laminate them and carry them with you on a ring or keep them in a card holder in a place where you'll be able to refer to them often.

It is our hope that this will be a tool that will help you truly learn these books for life.

1 CHRONICLES
Review: Preparing for the Temple

WHO:	**WHAT:**	**WHERE:**
David	Written After Exile to Encourage Returning Jews	Israel
	Content Similar to 2 Samuel	
	Written from a Priestly Perspective	
	Temple Is Unifying Theme	

Time Covered: 40 Years

2 CHRONICLES
Review: Judah's Spiritual Descent

WHO:	**WHAT:**	**WHERE:**
Solomon	Written After Exile to Encourage Returning Jews	United Kingdom of Israel
Kings of Judah	Content Similar to 1 and 2 Kings	Southern Kingdom of Judah
	Written from a Priestly Perspective	
	Temple Is Unifying Theme	

Time Covered: 433 Years

EZRA
Rebuilding the Temple

WHO:	**WHAT:**	**WHERE:**
Cyrus	Two Returns from Jerusalem to Persia (Formerly Babylonia)	Persia
Zerubbabel		Jerusalem
Ezra	Construction of Temple	
Haggai		
Zechariah	Restoration of People	

Time Covered: 91 Years

1 CHRONICLES
Review: Preparing for the Temple

Yours, O LORD, is the greatness and the power and the glory and the victory and the majesty, indeed everything that is in the heavens and the earth; Yours is the dominion, O LORD, and You exalt Yourself as head over all.

1 CHRONICLES 29:11

2 CHRONICLES
Review: Judah's Spiritual Descent

For the eyes of the LORD move to and fro throughout the earth that He may strongly support those whose heart is completely His.

2 CHRONICLES 16:9

EZRA
Rebuilding the Temple

For Ezra had set his heart to study the law of the LORD and to practice it, and to teach His statutes and ordinances in Israel.

EZRA 7:10

NEHEMIAH
Rebuilding the Wall

WHO:

Nehemiah

Ezra

WHAT:

Third Return from
Persia to Jerusalem

Wall Rebuilt
Around City

People's Covenant
with God Renewed

WHERE:

Persia

Jerusalem

Time Covered: 20 Years

ESTHER
Exiles' Providential Protection

WHO:

Ahasuerus

Haman

Mordecai

Esther

Jews in Persia

WHAT:

Jews Rescued from
Extinction by
Queen Esther

WHERE:

Persia

Time Covered: 10 Years

NEHEMIAH
Rebuilding the Wall

So the wall was completed. . . . When all our enemies heard of it . . . they recognized that this work had been accomplished with the help of our God.

NEHEMIAH 6:15-16

ESTHER
Exiles' Providential Protection

And who knows whether you have not attained royalty for such a time as this?

ESTHER 4:14

Introduction to THE POST-EXILIC BOOKS

By the end of 2 Kings, both the northern and southern kingdoms had been conquered. Israel, the northern kingdom, was conquered and scattered by Assyria. Almost 150 years later, the Babylonians destroyed Judah, the southern kingdom, and those who survived were exiled to Babylonia. The temple lay in ruins, the land was desolate, and it appeared that all hope was lost for the exiled remnant. As they struggled to survive as aliens in a strange culture and still maintain their Jewish identity, God was working behind the scenes in unimaginable ways. He had promised that Judah would be exiled for seventy years. But He had also promised to bring His people back to the land. In the books you are about to study, you will see that God keeps His promises.

During the seventy years Judah was in exile, the political world changed dramatically. The Persians defeated Babylonia and became the largest empire in the Near East. It was Persia that brought about an end to the Exile and allowed the Jews to return home, restore their temple, and build a wall around their beloved Jerusalem.

The Post-Exilic Books were written after the Exile, to and about this group of God's chosen people. First and 2 Chronicles were written to the people to encourage them in the land after they returned to Jerusalem, reminding them of their identity and heritage. Ezra and Nehemiah continue the history of the Jews from where it left off in 2 Kings. Esther is a beautiful story of the providential hand of God moving to protect His people. Chronologically, the Old Testament Historical Books end with Nehemiah. All of the Old Testament books following Nehemiah merely fit into the time period of these Historical Books.

I CHRONICLES

ONE

[Review: Preparing for the Temple]

Yours, O LORD, is the greatness and the power and the glory

and the victory and the majesty, indeed everything that is in

the heavens and the earth; Yours is the dominion, O LORD,

and You exalt Yourself as head over all.

1 CHRONICLES 29:11

I CHRONICLES
[Review: Preparing for the Temple]

INTRODUCTION

Many of those who traveled to Jerusalem after the Exile had never been there, nor had they ever seen the temple. Many more may have known little of the rich history of the people and the importance of their covenant relationship with God. After arriving in Jerusalem, the returning exiles were faced with hard work, great discouragement, and the lure of a godless society.

First and 2 Chronicles were written during this challenging time. In the earliest manuscripts, 1 and 2 Chronicles were one book, written from a spiritual perspective to encourage the returning remnant to love and obey God.

A detailed genealogy beginning with Adam and ending with those returning from Babylonian captivity begins the book of 1 Chronicles. The book then continues with a history of the reign of King David, covering much of the same material as 2 Samuel but from a spiritual rather than a political perspective. There is great emphasis on the preparations to build the temple and the organization of the Levites for temple service. The book ends with David's death and the ascension of his son Solomon to the throne.

Although there are many similarities between 2 Samuel and 1 Chronicles, the author of this book chose to omit David's sin with Bathsheba and his orders to murder her husband, Uriah. Instead, David's religious fervor and contribution to the spiritual life of Israel are the author's focus. This book was written to encourage the people to turn their eyes and hearts toward God and His temple and to worship the promise-keeping God who brought them back from exile.

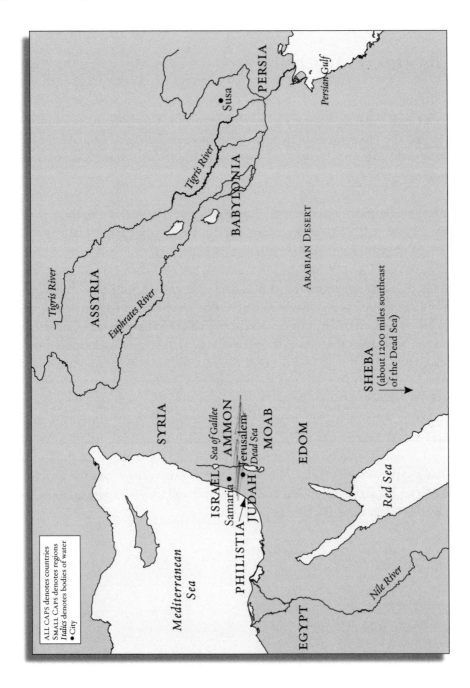

I CHRONICLES
[Review: Preparing for the Temple]

OVERVIEW

WHO: Author: Ezra (according to Jewish tradition)
Main Character: David

WHAT: The exiles review the historical record of David's preparation to build a place of worship—the temple

WHEN: Covers the forty-year reign of David (1011–971 BC)

WHERE: Israel

WHY: To prepare the remnant of Judah, returning after a seventy-year exile in Babylonia, for the rebuilding of the temple

I.   GENEALOGIES (1 CHRONICLES 1–9)

A. God traced the genealogy of Judah's twenty-one <u>Kings</u> from King David to the Exile.

B. God traced the genealogy of the Levites.

1. All Levites were to <u>Serve</u> in the temple.

2. Some Levites, Aaron's sons, were the priests.

II.   DAVID'S REIGN — PREPARING TO BUILD THE TEMPLE (1 CHRONICLES 10–29)

A. David prepared the place.

1. David captured the city of <u>Jerusalem</u>.

2. David returned the <u>ark</u> to Jerusalem.

B. David repeated the promise.

1. David's son <u>Solomon</u> would build the temple.

C. David prepared the provisions.

1. David used spoils of battles as building materials.

2. David bought land for the temple site _____ .

D. David prepared the people.

 1. David prepared the builders.

 2. David prepared the Levites and priests.

 3. David prepared himself to _die_____ .

 a. David declared Solomon king.

 b. David prepared Solomon to build.

 c. David prepared the people to give.

 d. David _worshipped_____ God.

 e. David prayed for the people.

APPLICATION

Now we are the temple of God. Just as the temple in Jerusalem would be restored, God wants to restore each of us — our lives, our families, and our nations. What has God done in the past that you need to remember to begin the restoration process?

I CHRONICLES
[Review: Preparing for the Temple]

LEARNING FOR LIFE

1. What happened to the nation of Israel before the writing of the book of 1 Chronicles, and what was about to happen?

2. What is the main theme of 1 Chronicles?

3. Why had the temple been destroyed?

4. The exiles were returning to the land, and God expressed the importance of rebuilding the temple.

   a. Who lived in the temple, and what took place there? *levites*

   b. Why was the temple so important to the nation of Israel?

5. Where or what is the temple today? (See 1 Corinthians 3:16; 6:19.) What do you learn from this study about what it takes to rebuild (or restore) your temple?

6. What has God revealed to you that needs restoration in your life? What are you going to do about it?

7. Jesus spoke of the temple in John 2:18-21. What did He say about it?

8. What is the most important lesson you learned today?

1 CHRONICLES
[Review: Preparing for the Temple]

DAY ONE

COMPLETE READ: None

QUICK READ: None

THE BIG PICTURE

Browse any ten books on the life of Anne Morrow Lindbergh, and their subject would be the same: Anne Morrow Lindbergh. But each author would be writing from his or her own individual viewpoint.

One author might focus on Anne's role as supportive wife to Charles Lindbergh, the famous aviator; another might detail the tragedy of the Lindbergh baby kidnapping and Anne's enduring grief as a result; yet another might focus on her impact as a writer. Same material — different emphasis. Because each author purposefully focused on a specific aspect of Anne Morrow Lindbergh, the information you would get from each portrayal would be complementary to the others, but unique.

Likewise, if you browse through the books of 1 and 2 Samuel and 1 and 2 Kings and then through 1 and 2 Chronicles, you might think 1 and 2 Chronicles cover the same subject as the previous four. And they do, but from completely different viewpoints. First and 2 Chronicles cover the same time period, some of the same people, and some of the same events as 1 and 2 Samuel and 1 and 2 Kings, yet their approach is unique. Miss it, and you miss a clear and crucial glimpse into the heart of God.

The following is a comparison of approaches.

To be a person is to have a story to tell.

—ISAK DINESEN
(pseudonym of Baroness Karen Blixen), Danish author of *Out of Africa*

SAMUEL AND KINGS	CHRONICLES
Centrality of the THRONE	Centrality of the TEMPLE
Perspective of the HISTORIAN	Perspective of the PRIEST
Emphasis on the POLITICAL	Emphasis on the RELIGIOUS
INCLUDES Kingdom of Israel	OMITS Kingdom of Israel
TONE: Indictment for Sin	TONE: Motivation for Holiness
End of Books: NO HOPE	End of Books: HOPE

FACT
First Chronicles devotes only one chapter to Saul, but nineteen to David.

The theme for 1 Chronicles, which we will begin studying on Day Two, is preparing for the temple. The building of the temple takes place in 2 Chronicles.

Tradition suggests that Ezra is the author of the Chronicles, which were written for the Jews returning to Jerusalem from the Babylonian exile in 458 BC. While 1 and 2 Chronicles are books of history, they are history written as a motivation for holiness. They restate some of the material from 1 and 2 Kings but omit whatever does not reinforce their purpose. A holy walk with God involved orderly and pure worship in the temple. So that which emphasized and honored the temple and the worship that took place there was included, stressed, and held high.

Israel's record of obedience was bleak. The books of Samuel and Kings detail the people's consistent rebellion as they chased after and gave their hearts to foreign gods. As a nation, they paid the price for that disobedience by being exiled in Babylonia for seventy years. Upon their return home, the writer of Chronicles told the story of their past once more, making clear to them God's desire for holiness, purity of worship, and a persistent seeking after Him.

One of the best summaries of this desire is 2 Chronicles 26:5. Describing the reign of King Uzziah, Ezra writes, "As long as he sought the LORD, God prospered him." God wanted the returning Israelites to get beyond chasing after other gods and to pursue only Him. The books of Chronicles were an encouragement to do just that.

How you can think
so well of us

And be the God
You are,

Is darkness to
my intellect,

But sunshine to
my heart.

—FREDERICK FABER,
nineteenth-century
English Oratorian and
devotional writer

In our individual journey and relationship with God, it is very easy and quite common to get stuck. Something comes between us and God. We know it. He knows it. And He is very consistent in pointing it out to us. Sometimes we try to ignore it. Sometimes we try to cover it with a Band-Aid. But unless we deal with it openly, honestly, and seriously, we can become hindered from moving on with Him.

Except for God, no one knows you better than you. Is there anything in your life that is making it difficult or impossible for you to move on with Him in your journey toward holiness? Describe it clearly.

Begin an open dialogue with God about the things that hinder your relationship and rely on His powerful grace as you wrestle through them.

MEMORY VERSE

Yours, O LORD, is the greatness and the power and the glory and the victory and the majesty, indeed everything that is in the heavens and the earth; Yours is the dominion, O LORD, and You exalt Yourself as head over all.

1 CHRONICLES 29:11

REVIEW IT!
The theme of 1 Chronicles is preparing for the temple.

I CHRONICLES
[Review: Preparing for the Temple]

DAY TWO

COMPLETE READ: Chapters 1–9
QUICK READ: Chapter 9

NOTABLE FEATURE NUMBER I

The book of 1 Chronicles falls naturally into two sections. As the following chart shows, the dominant theme of the book is the preparation for the building of the temple. Though this theme permeates the entire book, 28:11-19 summarizes the preparations involved. This theme extends into 2 Chronicles before construction actually takes place.

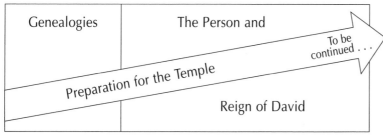

CHAPTERS 1–9	CHAPTERS 10–29
Genealogies	The Person and
Preparation for the Temple	Reign of David

Knowing that is the theme, it might be tempting to gloss over the first nine chapters of 1 Chronicles. Genealogies can be tedious, and they seem unrelated to the main point of the book. But if you are looking for a key to your past, trying to unravel a mystery, or filling in a blank spot on your family tree, then genealogies are fascinating. For this reason, the genealogies in chapters 1–9 are one of our Notable Features. If you did the Quick Read for today, you were probably surprised to find a few treasures hidden among the galaxy of names: jobs of the gatekeepers, responsibilities of the

Wisdom is to be gained only as we stand upon the shoulders of those who have gone before.

—LEARNED HAND, twentieth-century U.S. jurist who wrote *The Spirit of Liberty* and *The Bill of Rights*

singers, and even one man whose responsibility was overseeing things that were baked in pans!

Just for fun, and maybe for an insight or two, check out a few others:

- 1:19
- 2:3
- 3:4
- 4:9-10
- 4:21
- 4:27
- 5:1
- 5:25-26

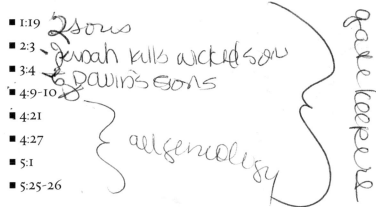

2 sons

Jenoah kills wicked son

David's sons

all genealogy

gatekeeper

The more we see and know of God, the more we realize and believe His great interest in and concern for people.

- He created us.
- He knows us intimately.
- He loves us.
- He gave His best for us — Jesus.
- He protects and provides for us.
- He longs for relationship with us.
- He works through us to bring about good.
- He plans to spend eternity with us.

Could it be that these genealogies are another way for God to demonstrate how intricately involved He is in the lives of people — and how critical they are to what He is doing in the world? Some may have cooperated, while others did not, but they are all characters in the great redemptive story He writes.

God obviously uses nature, circumstances, miracles — even angels — for His purposes. But above all, He uses people. Not because He has to, but because He chooses to.

When the people for whom Ezra was writing read the names he recorded, they would have been greatly encouraged. They would have been reminded again of their long, godly heritage and seen that God was still carrying out His promises. They would have understood that the line of David — through whom the Messiah would come — was still intact. And they would have seen that God had used people throughout history to be a blessing not only to their own generation but to the generations after them.

All of us have been blessed and indelibly marked by people God has placed in our lives.

Write down the names of those in your past (or present) whom God has used to bless you and briefly describe the ways they have been a blessing to you.

Over time, I have learned two things about my religious quest: First of all, that it is God who is seeking me, and who has myriad ways of finding me. Second, that my most substantial changes, in terms of religious conversion, come through other people. Even when I become convinced that God is absent from my life, others have a way of suddenly revealing God's presence.

—KATHLEEN NORRIS, author and poet

Is there anyone on your list you might want to send a note of appreciation?

MEMORY VERSE

Yours, O LORD, is the greatness and the power and the glory and the victory and the majesty, indeed everything that is in the heavens and the earth; Yours is the dominion, O LORD, and You exalt Yourself as head over all.

1 CHRONICLES 29:11

REVIEW IT!
Our Notable Feature Number 1 is the genealogies and their hidden treasures.

ICHRONICLES
[Review: Preparing for the Temple]

REMEMBER
Chronicles covers the same territory as Kings—but with a different slant.

DAY THREE

COMPLETE READ: Chapters 10–15
QUICK READ: Chapters 11–12

PROMINENT PLAYERS

"No man is an island" is an old phrase, but its truth is still relevant today.

To a significant degree, David did as well as he did because he was not an island. In your Quick Read for today, the writer of Chronicles named and described those people who surrounded David — his mighty men. He listed name after name after name, many of which we can't even pronounce! But please, persevere. Ignore these chapters, and you will miss something big — our Prominent Players.

First Chronicles 11:10 says, "Now these are the heads of the mighty men whom David had, who gave him strong support in his kingdom." The words "strong support" are a picture of strengthening and encouragement. These men didn't just vote for David. They didn't simply attend rallies honoring him. They came alongside him, helped carry the load, gave advice, fought in his battles, met his needs, and even fulfilled some of his wants.

Service can never become slavery to one who loves.

—J. L. MASSE

In 1 Chronicles 11:15-19, we find an interesting and unusual story. David had a want — not a need. And immediately, three of his mighty men jumped on it! But David's response to their act of service was very unexpected.

Read these verses and jot down any thoughts you have about or traits you see in the mighty men through their act of service and in David through his request and response.

Mighty Men

David

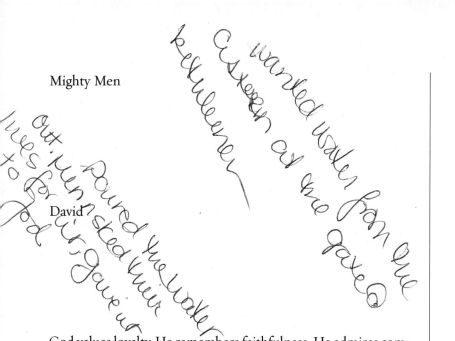

FACT
First Chronicles does
not record David's sin
with Bathsheba.

God values loyalty. He remembers faithfulness. He admires commitment. He treasures service. His Son would one day say, "Whoever wishes to become great among you shall be your servant" (Mark 10:43).

Are you a "mighty woman"? Is there someone you might come alongside to strengthen and encourage or whose load you could help carry? Name the person(s) and then list the ways you could come alongside them. Then thank God for giving you the privilege to be a mighty woman in the service of another.

*Friendship is one of the
sweetest joys of life.
Many might have failed
beneath the bitterness
of their trial had they
not found a friend.*

—CHARLES SPURGEON,
nineteenth-century
British preacher

If you sense you need to grow in this area, ask God to bless you with someone just waiting for the strength and encouragement you could bring to his or her life.

REVIEW IT!
Because of their encouragement to David, our Prominent Players are David's mighty men.

MEMORY VERSE

Yours, O LORD, is the greatness and the power and the glory and the victory and the majesty, indeed everything that is in the heavens and the earth; Yours is the dominion, O LORD, and You exalt Yourself as head over all.

1 CHRONICLES 29:11

I CHRONICLES
[Review: Preparing for the Temple]

DAY FOUR

COMPLETE READ: Chapters 16–22
QUICK READ: Chapters 16–17

REMEMBER
Chronicles is a
religious, not a
political, history.

NOTABLE FEATURE NUMBER 2

Alice Gray tells the following story:

> Mother Teresa attended a gathering with kings and presidents and statesmen from all over the world. They were there in their crowns and jewels and silks and Mother Teresa wore her sari held together by a safety pin. One of the noblemen spoke to her of her work with the poorest of the poor in Calcutta. He asked her if she didn't become discouraged because she saw so few successes in her ministry. Mother Teresa answered, "No, I do not become discouraged. You see, God has not called me to a ministry of success. He has called me to a ministry of mercy."[1]

If that same nobleman had lived during the events of 1 Chronicles 17, he may well have asked David a similar question about discouragement and success.

David accomplished something great when he retrieved the ark of the covenant from its temporary resting place and brought it to Jerusalem where it belonged. The ark represented the very presence of God to His people, and for it not to be in Jerusalem seemed an abomination to David. He had prepared a tent to house it, but he wanted to do more.

In 1 Chronicles 17:1 we read, "And it came about, when David dwelt in his house, that David said to Nathan the prophet,

In the realm of the sacred, what seems incomplete or unattainable may be abundance, after all.

—KATHLEEN NORRIS,
The Cloister Walk

'Behold, I am dwelling in a house of cedar, but the ark of the covenant of the LORD is under curtains.'" David saw that someone needed to build God a house worthy of Him, a house that could contain the ark of the covenant and so much more. And he knew he could do it. He knew people who could build, and he knew places where all the materials — gold, silver, cedar, everything — could be found.

But then something happened. Summarize what took place in 17:2-15.

handwritten: God Still don't know why God didn't let him build a temple but let Solomon

handwritten: This was what God asked of him

handwritten: Because he fought & shed blood, Isn't that what God asked of him?

Our experiences with abandonment and unwanted change are crisis moments when we must decide whether or not to leave behind the life that is gone forever. We can do that only if we believe in the ongoing creativity of God, who brings light and beauty to the dark clouds of our losses in life.

—M. CRAIG BARNES, When God Interrupts

David's great dream came crashing down. He was hoping to build the temple of the Lord, but instead he would be relegated to merely making plans, gathering materials, and hiring workmen for this house of all houses. His son Solomon would have the privilege and honor of building God's temple. But instead of being dejected or discouraged, David embraced the news that his ministry would be one of preparation, not of building. Our Notable Feature Number 2 is David's joyful acceptance of God's ministry choice for his life.

In 17:16-27, David responded with true humility and genuine submission to God. It was not spiritual pretense. What do you see about David and God in these verses that enabled David to face disappointment?

How could these same truths encourage you to respond to disappointment with a genuine heart?

Blessed is he who has found his work; let him ask no other blessedness.

—Thomas Carlyle, Scottish essayist and historian of the nineteenth century

Memory Verse

> Yours, O Lord, is the greatness and the power and the glory and the victory and the majesty, indeed everything that is in the heavens and the earth; Yours is the dominion, O Lord, and You exalt Yourself as head over all.
>
> 1 Chronicles 29:11

REVIEW IT!
Our Notable Feature Number 2 is David's joyful acceptance of God's ministry for him.

I CHRONICLES
[Review: Preparing for the Temple]

DAY FIVE

COMPLETE READ: Chapters 23–29
QUICK READ: Chapters 28–29

A TIMELESS PRINCIPLE

Have you ever walked closely with someone who knew he was dying or spoken with someone about her impending death? You may have been challenged and inspired by another's thoughts and words as he faced the end of his earthly life. If you have ever been at someone's bedside as she drew her last breath, you know that the moment of death is a sacred one.

In your Quick Read for today, King David faced his own mortality. The shepherd boy turned king had lived a long, full, rich life. He had walked with God through victory and defeat, joy and sorrow, clarity and confusion, holiness and sinfulness. He had progressed from the strong but simple faith of his great encounter with Goliath to the seasoned but still solid faith of his final encounter with death. And we have the privilege of reading what may have been his last publicly spoken words — words revealing that David finished his life well with complete trust in God. This is our Timeless Principle.

Chapters 28–29 contain David's last recorded words.

I am ready to meet God face to face tonight and look into those eyes of infinite holiness, for all my sins are covered by the atoning blood.
—R. A. TORREY,
U.S. Congregational clergyman and evangelist

Summarize in your own words what David talked about.

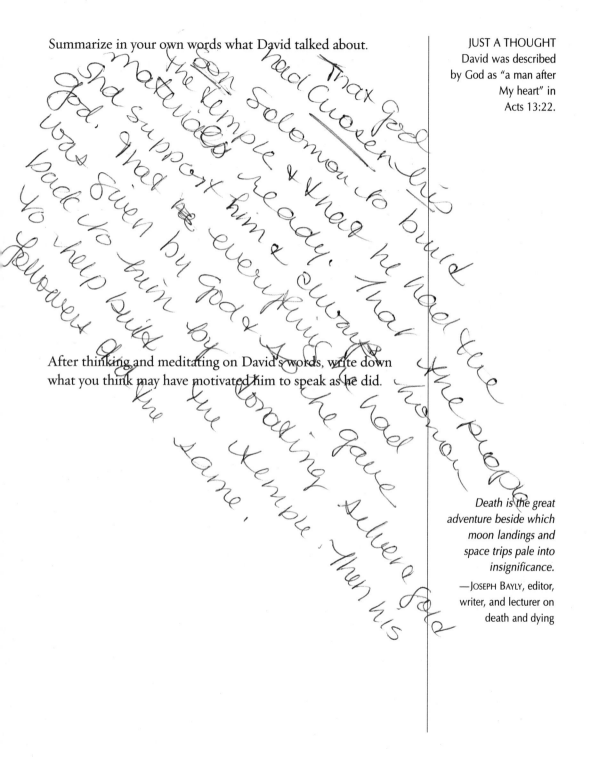

After thinking and meditating on David's words, write down
what you think may have motivated him to speak as he did.

JUST A THOUGHT
David was described
by God as "a man after
My heart" in
Acts 13:22.

*Death is the great
adventure beside which
moon landings and
space trips pale into
insignificance.*

—JOSEPH BAYLY, editor,
writer, and lecturer on
death and dying

What in your life gives you hope that, given the opportunity, you will be able to respond in a similar way?

MEMORY VERSE

Yours, O LORD, is the greatness and the power and the glory and the victory and the majesty, indeed everything that is in the heavens and the earth; Yours is the dominion, O LORD, and You exalt Yourself as head over all.

I CHRONICLES 29:11

I CHRONICLES
[Review: Preparing for the Temple]

REVIEW

1. The theme of I Chronicles is ___*peparing*___ for the temple.

2. Our Notable Feature Number I is the ___*geneablogies*___ and their hidden treasures.

3. Because of their encouragement to David, our Prominent Players are ___*Davids*___ mighty men.

4. Our Notable Feature Number 2 is ___*Davids*___ joyful acceptance of God's ministry for him.

5. "Yours, O LORD, is the greatness and the power and the glory and the victory and the majesty, indeed ___*everything*___ that is in the heavens and the earth; Yours is the dominion, O LORD, and You exalt Yourself as head over all."

I CHRONICLES 29:___*11*___

Prayer list

Nadine Wall, Bonnie Jackson's friend
+ Darby's friend.

- Charlotte Lamb.

Todd Peterson - and pain

Angie's niece cut her hand.

Haley Barnabei.

Roe's brother

Owen & her brother Michael divertic
C.Diff
mac.degen.

2 CHRONICLES

[Review: Judah's Spiritual Descent]

For the eyes of the LORD move to and fro throughout

the earth that He may strongly support those

whose heart is completely His.

2 CHRONICLES 16:9

2 CHRONICLES
[Review: Judah's Spiritual Descent]

INTRODUCTION

Second Chronicles continues the history of Israel that began in 1 Chronicles. Much of the material in Chronicles is taken from 1 and 2 Kings, but with one marked difference: The northern kingdom of Israel is almost completely ignored. Israel did not have the temple. It did not have the ark of the covenant. It did not have a king from the line of David. It never had a righteous king, and its people became increasingly wicked. Though they had a form of godliness, they continually worshiped other gods. For these reasons, the history of the northern kingdom was not as instructive to the spiritual encouragement of the remnant.

The remnant of Judah needed to understand that the future of their nation rested on their love and devotion to God. They had to learn from the past to set a right course for the future. One way to learn was by looking at the kings of Judah, all from the line of David. In Judah's past, twelve kings were labeled "bad," eight were called "good," and five of those eight brought about spiritual revivals in the land. A second emphasis for learning holiness was recalling the importance of the temple: the building of the temple, the consecration of the temple, the neglect of the temple, the revival of temple worship, and in the end, the destruction of the temple.

The history of Judah reveals that God cares deeply about His people and that He is long-suffering and faithful. But history also makes it clear that God will bring about judgment and discipline if His people refuse to worship Him alone. Second Chronicles is a review of the history of Judah and a message of encouragement and inspiration to love God deeply, to worship Him purely, and to obey Him completely.

2CHRONICLES

[Review: Judah's Spiritual Descent]

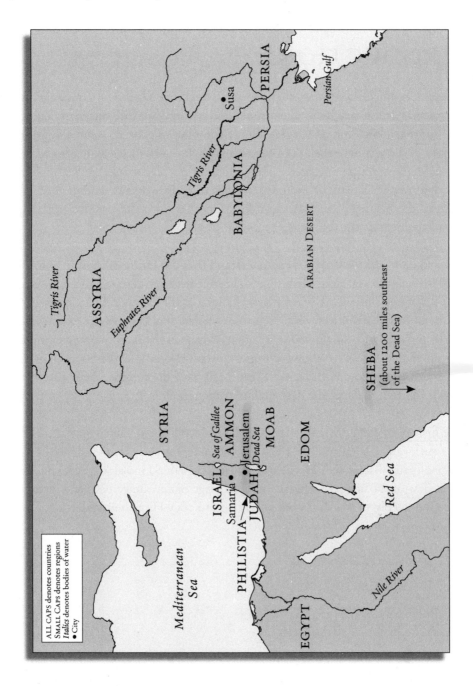

ALL CAPS denotes countries
SMALL CAPS denotes regions
Italics denotes bodies of water
• City

PERSIA

Persian Gulf

• Susa

Tigris River

BABYLONIA

Tigris River

ASSYRIA

Euphrates River

ARABIAN DESERT

SHEBA
(about 1200 miles southeast
of the Dead Sea)

SYRIA

Sea of Galilee

ISRAEL

AMMON

Samaria •

Jerusalem •

Dead Sea

JUDAH

MOAB

PHILISTIA

EDOM

Red Sea

*Mediterranean
Sea*

EGYPT

Nile River

[handwritten top margin: 1st 9 chapters Israel < 10th chapter Judah + Benjamin]

2CHRONICLES
[Review: Judah's Spiritual Descent]

OVERVIEW

WHO: Author: Ezra (according to Jewish tradition)
Main Characters: Solomon (chapters 1–9), all the kings of Judah (chapters 10–36)

WHAT: Continues the historical review of Judah and the Davidic lineage

WHEN: 971–538 BC

WHERE: United kingdom of Israel (chapters 1–10), only the southern kingdom of Judah (chapters 11–36)

WHY: Written to encourage those returning to Judah after the Exile in Babylonia to learn from the past and live in faithfulness to God

I. THE NATION OF ISRAEL IN ITS _____Glory_____: LOOK TO THE PAST (2 CHRONICLES 1–9)

   A. King Solomon received _discernment_ _wisdom_ from God.

   B. Solomon built the temple and it symbolized the ~~importance~~ _?, symbolic_ _presence_ of God in the nation.

      1. It took seven years to build the temple.

      2. All of the stones were cut off-site.

      3. The temple was built on Mount Moriah.

      4. The temple was built with cedar, silver, bronze, and gold.

      5. The temple contained no idols.

      6. There was only one temple in Israel because there was only one God.

      7. The temple was thirty feet by ninety feet and forty-five feet high.

      8. The temple had only two interior rooms.

      9. Only the priests entered the temple.

   C. The nation of Israel enjoyed _peace_, prosperity, and prestige under Solomon's rule. _all his life_

II. THE NATION OF JUDAH IN ITS DECLINE AND _DESTRUCTION_ :
LEARN FOR THE PRESENT (2 CHRONICLES 10)

A. There were twenty kings in Judah.

1. There were ___8___ good kings in Judah and twelve evil kings.

a. _Ahaz_ was an example of an evil king.

b. _Hezekiah (Ahaz's son)_ was an example of a good king.

2. There were five revivals recorded in 2 Chronicles.

B. Jerusalem and the temple were destroyed by Babylon in ~~586~~ 584 BC.

C. Many of the people were taken into _exile_ to Babylon.

Baal worshiper sacrificed son by fire

III. THE NATION YET TO BE: LIVE FOR THE FUTURE (2 CHRONICLES 36)

A. Jeremiah (29:10) had prophesied before the fall of Jerusalem that the people would return from exile after seventy years.

B. God chose Cyrus, king of Persia, to allow the people to go back to Judah to rebuild the temple. *Persia had conquered Babylon*

APPLICATION

The center of your worship will determine the success of your life.

why did they even led the temple thrive?

2CHRONICLES
[Review: Judah's Spiritual Descent]

LEARNING FOR LIFE

prophet ?

1. Review the history of 1 and 2 Chronicles.

2. What was the single greatest factor in bringing about revival? Do you think the leadership of a country can encourage or discourage religious fervor today?

3. Why do you think the author deliberately left out the dark side of Solomon's life?

Trying to encourge people

4. If you were getting ready to return to Jerusalem with the remnant, how would this book encourage you?

5. Consider the importance of the temple in this book. Why do you think it was so strongly emphasized?

6. What role did obedience to God play in the welfare of the people? Do you believe it is still as important today?

7. What is the most important thing you learned today?

2 CHRONICLES
[Review: Judah's Spiritual Descent]

FACT
The temple was ninety feet long and thirty feet wide.

DAY ONE

COMPLETE READ: Chapters 6:1-17; 7
QUICK READ: Chapters 6:1-17; 7

THE BIG PICTURE

Because 1 and 2 Chronicles were originally written as one book — Greek translators later separated them — some of the information you learned about 1 Chronicles is also true of 2 Chronicles.

- Ezra is believed to be the author.

- It was written for the exiles returning from Babylonia in 458 BC.

- It was written to encourage them to seek God.

- It covers material also found in the books of Kings, but from a different perspective.

First Chronicles was all about preparation for building the temple. David had desperately wanted to build it for the Lord — what a legacy it would be! But God had other plans and instead chose David's son Solomon to be the builder.

If the Lord be with us, we have no cause to fear. His eye is upon us, His arm over us, His ear open to our prayer—His grace sufficient, His promise unchangeable.

—JOHN NEWTON, eighteenth-century English clergyman, hymnist, and sailor

As we saw, David fell in line with God's heart and plan and immediately adopted a servant role, making as many preparations as he possibly could. Solomon's job was significantly simplified because of David's work behind the scenes.

The first nine chapters of 2 Chronicles are about Solomon, but more importantly, they are about building the temple, our theme for the book.

Second Chronicles 7:11 signifies a major turning point in the book when it says, "Thus Solomon finished the house of the LORD." No longer is the emphasis on constructing the temple, but on the people orienting their lives around it — not around the building itself, but around Who and what the building represented.

The temple represented God's presence among His people. It was a constant, visible reminder of God's desire to be worshiped, and through it He identified with His people and they with Him.

Read 2 Chronicles 7:1-3 again. Record the phrases that describe the scene and consider how you might have felt if you had been an eyewitness. *awed and amazed*

AMAZING!
David had provided
3,750 tons of pure gold
for the temple.

Upon completion of the temple, all the kings succeeding Solomon (see chapters 10–36) would be evaluated on the basis of their relationship to the temple and to the God of the temple.

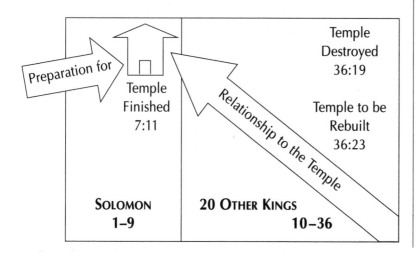

Preparation for

Temple Finished 7:11

Relationship to the Temple

Temple Destroyed 36:19

Temple to be Rebuilt 36:23

SOLOMON 1–9

20 OTHER KINGS 10–36

What I believe about God is the most important thing about me.
—A. W. TOZER, author and theologian of the twentieth century

God could not have been more clear about His command for these kings. Reread 2 Chronicles 7:11-22 and summarize in your own words the promises of blessing for following God and the promises of judgment for forsaking Him.

Now jump ahead almost four hundred years to the end of the story in 2 Chronicles 36:15-19. What thoughts and feelings do you have as you read these verses?

You can understand the anger + disappointment God had this people

MEMORY VERSE

For the eyes of the LORD move to and fro throughout the earth that He may strongly support those whose heart is completely His.

2 CHRONICLES 16:9

2 CHRONICLES
[Review: Judah's Spiritual Descent]

DAY TWO

COMPLETE READ: Chapters 1–9
QUICK READ: Chapter 9

A PROMINENT PLAYER

Even though Solomon's reign covers only one-fourth of 2 Chronicles, he remains the most significant figure in the story and is, therefore, our Prominent Player. God chose Solomon, the son of David and Bathsheba, to be the third king of the nation. Saul, David, and Solomon reigned during the 120-year period of the united kingdom. But following Solomon's death, the nation divided into two kingdoms — the northern kingdom of Israel and the southern kingdom of Judah.

Solomon's reign was brilliant. His crowning triumph was the completion of the temple, which God's glory inhabited in a stunning blaze of fire. Much of Solomon's success resulted from the answer he gave to a question asked by God at the beginning of his reign.

Read 2 Chronicles 1:7-13 and in your own words describe the significance of that answer.

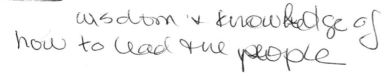

wisdom & knowledge of how to lead the people

DID YOU KNOW?
More than 150,000 workers were used to build the temple.

Our greatest claim to nobility is our created capacity to know God, to be in personal relationship with Him, to love Him and to worship Him. Indeed, we are most truly human when we are on our knees before our Creator.

—JOHN STOTT, author and Christian leader

Solomon accumulated wealth, land, wisdom, and power like few kings in history ever had. His fame grew as steadily as his wealth, reaching far into other parts of the world — and even piquing the curiosity of the queen of Sheba. Wanting to see this king for herself, she traveled over 1,200 miles to Jerusalem for a personal visit. Her visit is recorded in your Quick Read for today, 2 Chronicles 9:1-12.

What impressed her? What is the significance of verse 8?

That she recognized that God had provided & was pleased c Solomon.

The writer of 2 Chronicles did not include a full account of Solomon's reign. To catch a glimpse of the darker side, read 1 Kings 11:1-10. As you read, remember that Solomon built God's temple and that the temple was the symbol of His presence among the people, reminding them to seek Him only. What do these verses say that contradicts this intent?

That Solomon's wives turned his heart to many other gods.

When you live in a Christianity of tips and techniques, you trivialize sin. Sin is [considered] something external. It's running stop signs. It's drinking too much. It's smoking. But God calls sin adultery of the heart. It is what you give your heart away to other than the heart of God.
—JOHN ELDREDGE, Preaching Today

Solomon died with a divided heart — partially given to his God and partially given to the gods of his many wives. That divided heart would yield a divided kingdom for the next generation.

What are some issues or areas in your life that might divide your spiritual loyalty?

MEMORY VERSE

For the eyes of the LORD move to and fro throughout the earth that He may strongly support those whose heart is completely His.

2 CHRONICLES 16:9

REVIEW IT!
Solomon is a Prominent Player in 2 Chronicles.

2 CHRONICLES
[Review: Judah's Spiritual Descent]

REMEMBER
First and 2 Chronicles were originally written as one book.

DAY THREE

COMPLETE READ: Chapters 10–18
QUICK READ: Chapters 11–12

A CRUCIAL CHAPTER

The first year of marriage can set a lasting tone. The first year of school can significantly determine a child's learning posture. The first president of a country can lay down precedents that become difficult to change. Firsts are significant. They establish patterns — good or bad.

Solomon's son Rehoboam represented one of those "firsts" for God's chosen people. He was the first king of Israel to follow the Big Three: Saul, David, and Solomon. Very soon after becoming king, his choices caused the division of one nation into two: Israel in the north and Judah in the south. As the first king of Judah, Rehoboam established practices that became the spiritual battleground for succeeding kings over the next 350 years.

As you can see in the chart that follows, Rehoboam began well.

Great is the art of beginning, but greater is the art of ending.
—HENRY WADSWORTH LONGFELLOW, American poet of the nineteenth century

Years 1–3	Year 4	Years 5–17
Followed the Lord	Forsook the Lord	Forbearance of the Lord
11:17	12:1	12:7,12

For the first three years of his reign, he listened to God and obeyed Him (2 Chronicles 11:4), thereby establishing a great pattern for the kings of Judah. But it didn't last. He soon forsook the Lord and established another pattern — one that not only was evil but also became deeply entrenched. Once that happened, it was a steep slide down for Rehoboam — and for the nation. Only God's forbearance kept things from becoming worse than they already were.

Chapter 12 is our Crucial Chapter. Verse 1 of this chapter says simply that Rehoboam "forsook the law of the Lord." The writer of Chronicles did not detail the full extent of Rehoboam's forsaking, but 1 Kings 14:21-24 tells us more. Read these verses and summarize in your own words how Rehoboam forsook God's laws.

Second Chronicles demonstrates God's desire that His people have a proper relationship with Him and proper respect toward His symbolic presence in and surrounding the temple. Contrast this desire with what you just read in 1 Kings 14:21-24.

There is another stage to be reached, where all consciousness of ourselves and of what God is doing through us is eliminated. A saint is never consciously a saint; a saint is consciously dependent on God.

—OSWALD CHAMBERS, *My Utmost for His Highest*

Rehoboam's epitaph could have come directly from 2 Chronicles 12:14: "He did evil because he did not set his heart to seek the LORD."

For nearly 350 years, the nation lived in constant tension between the first bad patterns established by Rehoboam and attempts to eradicate them and form new, good patterns. Every succeeding king would be evaluated on the basis of what pattern he chose.

What "first" patterns did you establish in your personal relationship with God that have proven to be healthy and good? Write a few of them down and then savor their resulting blessings for a few moments.

REVIEW IT!
A Crucial Chapter in 2 Chronicles is chapter 12 in which Rehoboam forsakes God.

MEMORY VERSE

For the eyes of the LORD move to and fro throughout the earth that He may strongly support those whose heart is completely His.

2 CHRONICLES 16:9

2 CHRONICLES
[Review: Judah's Spiritual Descent]

REMEMBER
King Solomon built
the temple.

DAY FOUR

COMPLETE READ: Chapters 19–27
QUICK READ: Chapter 19

A NOTABLE FEATURE

AN AUTOBIOGRAPHY IN FIVE SHORT PARAGRAPHS

By Portia Nelson

1. I walk down the street. There is a deep hole in the sidewalk. I fall in. I am lost. I am helpless. It isn't my fault. It takes forever to find a way out.
2. I walk down the street. There is a deep hole in the sidewalk. I pretend I don't see it. I fall in. I can't believe I'm in the same place, but it isn't my fault. It still takes a long time to get out.
3. I walk down the street. There is a deep hole in the sidewalk. I see it is there. I still fall in. It's a habit. My eyes are open. I know where I am. It is my fault. I get out immediately.
4. I walk down the street. There is a deep hole in the sidewalk. I walk around it.
5. I walk down a different street.[1]

Revival is nothing else than a new beginning of obedience to God.

—CHARLES FINNEY, nineteenth-century U.S. educator, evangelist, and itinerant preacher; president of Oberlin College

The history of Judah appears to be one of walking down the same street and falling in the same hole. Yet even in the midst of the people's repetitive sin pattern, there were times — significant times — when they chose a different street. No hole. No fall. These were times of revival.

Throughout history, for reasons known only to Him, God has

initiated revival for His people. And revival always involves repentance: rejecting the depravity of the old street and choosing to walk down a different street. Thus our Notable Feature in 2 Chronicles is the occurrence of periodic revivals.

When we read about revivals in 2 Chronicles, they encourage and challenge us spiritually. Reading about others turning their backs on sin and seeking God again becomes a mirror for us — helping us to see choices we need to make in our lives.

The following passages are examples of periodic revivals during those 350 years. As you read the verses, record your thoughts on these questions by filling in the chart: What seemed to cause revival? What did the king and people do? How did God respond? What commitments were made?

Passage	Cause of Revival	Actions of King and People	Response by God	Commitments Made
14:1-7	Asa removed Idols & made Judah Seek God	Sought God	Peace in the land	build wells to protect city
15:8-15	restoration of alter remove idols	sought God		
29:20-36	Sin offerings	atone for sins		restore service to God.
31:1	Israelites smashed sacred pillars of Judah			

All of life is repentance.
—Martin Luther,
German theologian and
leader of the Protestant
Reformation

Passage	Cause of Revival	Actions of King and People	Response by God	Commitments Made
34:1-7	Josiah sought after god purged high places		R	
34:14-21, 29-33; 35:16-19	gave $ to the temple Read from the book of the covenant			

Did you notice that for Judah, walking down a different street always involved seeking God, cleansing His temple, and committing to follow Him wholeheartedly in repentance, humility, and proper worship? How can you apply this practice to your own life?

Memory Verse

For the eyes of the LORD move to and fro throughout the earth that He may strongly support those whose heart is completely His.

2 Chronicles 16:9

REVIEW IT!
A Notable Feature of 2 Chronicles is the occurrence of periodic revivals.

2 CHRONICLES
[Review: Judah's Spiritual Descent]

INSIGHT
Whenever the kings sought the Lord, so did the people.

DAY FIVE

COMPLETE READ: Chapters 28–36
QUICK READ: Chapters 15:1-2; 19:3

A TIMELESS PRINCIPLE

The temple — the symbol of the presence of God among His people — is the theme of 2 Chronicles. To seek His presence, to live in His presence, to shun everything that hinders being in His presence — this is the passionate message of the book. And though the message is ancient, it is still desperately needed today. Seeking God's presence is a Timeless Principle.

We need not list all our distractions. They are numerous, and we know them all too well. Instead, write down the one thing that is distracting you the most at this moment.

When you are not the One who fills me, I am soon filled with endless thoughts and concerns that divide me and tear me away from You. Only You can set my heart at rest, only You can let me dwell in Your presence.

—HENRI NOUWEN, twentieth-century priest and author

Clever tactics cannot destroy our distractions. They do not yield to tricks, compromise, neglect, or rules. Our focus should not be on gaining power over our distractions but on seeking power from God. Take a moment to pray for this power as A. W. Tozer did:

O God and Father, I repent of my sinful preoccupation with visible things. The world has been too much with me. Thou hast been here and I knew it not. I have been blind to Thy Presence. Open my eyes that I may behold Thee in and around me. For Christ's sake, Amen.[2]

O God, quicken to life every power within me, that I may lay hold on eternal things. Open my eyes that I may see; give me acute spiritual perception; enable me to taste Thee and know that Thou art good. Make heaven more real to me than any earthly thing has ever been. Amen.[3]

Seeking God's presence was also the passion of the psalmist:

> As the deer pants for the water brooks,
> So my soul pants for You, O God.
> My soul thirsts for God, for the living God;
> When shall I come and appear before God? (Psalm 42:1-2)

> O God, You are my God; I shall seek You earnestly;
> My soul thirsts for You, my flesh yearns for You,
> In a dry and weary land where there is no water. (Psalm 63:1)

> One thing I have asked from the LORD, that shall I seek;
> That I may dwell in the house of the LORD all the days of
>   my life,
> To behold the beauty of the LORD
> And to meditate in His temple. (Psalm 27:4)

What does seeking God mean to you, and what does it look like in your life?

DID YOU KNOW?
The last two verses of 2 Chronicles are the same as the first two verses of Ezra.

Of the heavenly things God has shown me, I can speak but a little word, no more than a honeybee can carry away on its foot from an overflowing jar.

—MECHTILD OF MAGDEBURG, thirteenth-century mystic writer

Recall a time or period of time when you sensed the presence of God in your life in a very real way.

Progress in our seeking makes us more desirous still. Saint Bernard put it this way:

> We taste Thee, O Thou Living Bread,
> And long to feast upon Thee still:
> We drink of Thee, the Fountainhead
> And thirst our souls from Thee to fill.[4]

Remember, "our pursuit of God is successful just because He is forever seeking to manifest Himself to us."[5]

If you were to give closer attention to seeking God, how would you go about it?

MEMORY VERSE

For the eyes of the LORD move to and fro throughout the earth that He may strongly support those whose heart is completely His.

2 CHRONICLES 16:9

2 CHRONICLES
[Review: Judah's Spiritual Descent]

REVIEW

1. The theme of 2 Chronicles is ___building___ the temple.

2. ___Solomon___ is a Prominent Player in 2 Chronicles.

3. A Crucial Chapter in 2 Chronicles is chapter 12 in which ___Rehoboam___ forsakes God.

4. A Notable Feature of 2 Chronicles is the occurrence of periodic ___revivals___

5. "For the eyes of the LORD move to and fro throughout the earth that He may strongly support those whose ___heart___ is completely His."

2 CHRONICLES 16:___9___

Rich - Portugal.
Stacy Safino
Larry Zahara } passed away

Todd - doing well; another surgery in a few mos.
Charlotte Lamb - oncol. appt - head. 1cm
200 !!
Jill - oncol. appt c Reddy, monday
Haley.

Jill's friend Linda Bailey

EZRA

[Rebuilding the Temple]

was a scribe & also wrote Chronicles & Kings

For Ezra had set his heart to study the law of the LORD and to

practice it, and to teach His statutes and ordinances in Israel.

EZRA 7:10

THREE

EZRA
[Rebuilding the Temple]

INTRODUCTION

For seventy years the people lived in exile in Babylonia. Then, just as He had promised, God moved kings and shaped nations to allow His people to return to the land. The book of Ezra chronicles the first two returns of the people from Babylonia to Jerusalem. It continues the history of Judah from where 2 Chronicles left off.

Through God's intervention, the people returned to the land under the leadership of Zerubbabel. But of the two or three million Jews living in exile at the time, only about fifty thousand — a remnant — returned to their homeland. Life was comfortable in Babylonia, so comfortable that many refused to leave. Most of those who returned were born in captivity. They had never seen the temple or Jerusalem. They had not sacrificed offerings nor experienced the beauty and awe of temple worship. Even so, these people left everything behind and traveled over nine hundred miles back to the land God had given them. This was a tremendous step into the unknown for many. Under Zerubbabel's leadership, and in spite of great persecution by the Jerusalem populace, the rebuilding of the temple was finally completed.

Eighty years later, under the capable leadership of Ezra, another group of about two thousand returned to Jerusalem. There they found the people spiritually bankrupt and morally lax. Ezra the priest began to work on rebuilding the people's spiritual life, and because of his commitment and prayers, the people eventually repented and turned back to the living God.

The past shd be a rudder to guide us, not an anchor to hold us.

E ZRA
[Rebuilding the Temple]

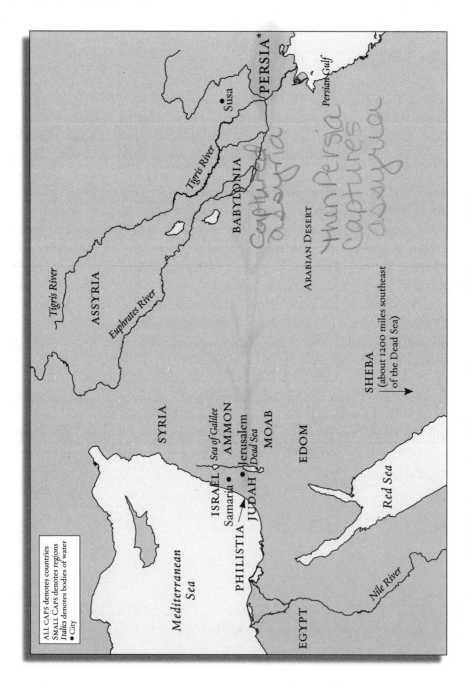

*In the book of Ezra, most of the area on this map was under the control of the Persian empire.

E ZRA
[Rebuilding the Temple]

King of Persia = Cyrus

OVERVIEW

WHO: Author: Ezra (according to Jewish tradition)
Main Characters: Cyrus, Zerubbabel, Ezra, Haggai, Zechariah

WHAT: After 70 years in captivity, a remnant returned to rebuild the temple in Jerusalem

WHEN: Covers 91 years (536–445 BC)

WHERE: Persia, Jerusalem

WHY: Records the history of the returned remnant and the restoration of the temple, as well as the spiritual revival of God's children. We see that God is faithful in keeping His promises

I. FIRST RETURN: REMNANT REBUILT (EZRA 1–6)

A. Released Remnant — Fulfillment of Prophecy (Ezra 1–2)

1. The people were given two choices: _____return_____ or _____support_____ the return.

2. A _____census_____ was taken to number the returning remnant.

B. Rebuilding Began (Ezra 3)

1. _____Zerubabel_____ was God's choice to lead the remnant home.

2. The people _____prayed_____ to God because they were motivated by _____fear_____.

3. Protected by God, the _____foundation_____ was laid

many were born in captivity & so not wanted to go

50,000 people returned 4 mos. journey

C. Restoration Hindered by Opposition (Ezra 4)

1. The enemy's first tactic was _____compromise_____.

2. The second tactic employed was _____discouragement_____.

3. The third tactic used was _____accusation_____.

D. Remnant Rallied by Prophets (Ezra 5)

E. Rebuilding of Temple Completed (Ezra 6) - - - *King Darius*

II. SECOND RETURN: REMNANT REVIVED (EZRA 7–10)

2nd trip

A. Readied for Return Under Ezra (Ezra 7–8)

1. The return began as _Ezra_ found favor with the king and the people were allowed to leave. *Only about 1,500 people*

2. The remnant was counted and prepared through prayer and returned safely to Israel.

58 yr period of time.

B. Recognition of Sin by Ezra (Ezra 9)

1. Reports of _unfaithfulness_ reached Ezra.

2. _Rebellion_ of the people grieved Ezra. He mourned as the fearful people were summoned.

9:6–15 Ezra confessed the sins of the people.

C. Renewal of Covenant (Ezra 10)

1. _Restoration_ of Israel's relationship with God began.

2. _Repentance_ brought revival.

APPLICATION

Ezra gives a picture of God's grace. When we are willing to return to Him and admit our sins (repent), He is always faithful to forgive us and restore us to our former relationship with Him (revival). Israel had sinned, suffered the consequences of that sin, and then was restored by God to Himself. We are recipients of that same grace!

EZRA
[Rebuilding the Temple]

LEARNING FOR LIFE

1. Relate some of the history that led up to the events in the book of Ezra.

2. What is Ezra's main theme? Can you recall a time of brokenness in your life that God restored?

3. Give the details (circumstances, leaders, and so on) of the two returns to Jerusalem from Persia.

4. List the sequence of events that led to the work on the temple being stopped. What happened to get it started again?

5. Identify some of the opposition that the returning exiles faced and record the results. Share a time when you were tempted to quit or were slowed down by difficulty or trials.

6. How did Ezra show his trust in God when beginning his journey to Jerusalem? How could we imitate this in our lives today?

7. Even though the temple had been restored, the people were in need of a spiritual revival. Relate a time when you experienced a restoration in your life — with another person or with God.

8. In what ways could Jesus be seen as a restorer? (See 2 Corinthians 5:17.)

9. What can you take away from this teaching today that will make a difference in your life?

E ZRA
[Rebuilding the Temple]

DAY ONE

COMPLETE READ: Chapters 1–2
QUICK READ: Chapters 1–2

THE BIG PICTURE

Going back to an old home place that has been neglected for years can be depressing. Weeds have grown up. Buildings have deteriorated. The past glory is gone. And the future promises hard work — lots of hard work — if restoration is to happen.

This is the scene we discover as we begin to study the books of Ezra and Nehemiah. Cyrus, the king of Persia, had ordered that the Israelite exiles leave Persia and return home to Jerusalem (Ezra 1:1-3), but what they found there was depressing. Seventy years before, the city, the walls, and the temple were severely damaged when Nebuchadnezzar, king of Babylonia, conquered the city. The task of restoring and rebuilding would be a daunting one, yet the people were excited. The theme of Ezra is rebuilding the home place.

The chronology of the post-exilic period can be confusing. The timeline that follows will help you understand the relationships between foreign kings, Israelite leaders, and major tasks. To give a complete picture, the timeline also includes the books of Nehemiah and Esther, which, along with Ezra, tell the history of the post-exilic period.

As the timeline indicates, the book of Ezra has two distinct parts separated by fifty-eight years. The next chart gives the key information for each part.

The prophet Ezra is believed to be the author of the book that bears his name, along with the books of the Chronicles. In 1 and

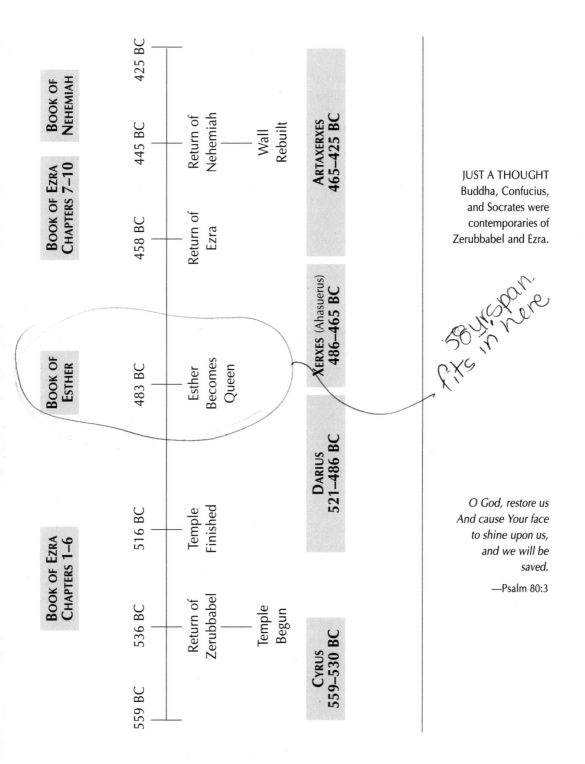

BOOK OF NEHEMIAH

BOOK OF EZRA CHAPTERS 7–10

BOOK OF ESTHER

BOOK OF EZRA CHAPTERS 1–6

425 BC

445 BC — Return of Nehemiah — Wall Rebuilt

458 BC — Return of Ezra

483 BC — Esther Becomes Queen

516 BC — Temple Finished

536 BC — Return of Zerubbabel — Temple Begun

559 BC

ARTAXERXES 465–425 BC

XERXES (Ahasuerus) **486–465 BC**

DARIUS 521–486 BC

CYRUS 559–530 BC

58 yr. span fits in here

JUST A THOUGHT
Buddha, Confucius, and Socrates were contemporaries of Zerubbabel and Ezra.

O God, restore us
And cause Your face
to shine upon us,
and we will be
saved.

—Psalm 80:3

DID YOU NOTICE?
The book of Ezra
begins (see 1:1-13)
almost exactly as
the previous book,
2 Chronicles, ends
(see 36:22-23).

EZRA 1–6		**EZRA 7–10**
Return of ZERUBBABEL	Book of Esther	Return of EZRA
Rebuilding the TEMPLE	58-Year Gap	Rebuilding the PEOPLE
Emphasis: HOUSE of God		Emphasis: WORD of God
536–516 BC		458–445 BC

*Do not look forward to
the changes and
chances of this life in
fear; rather look to
them with full hope
that, as they arise, God,
whose you are, will
deliver you out of
them. He is your
keeper. He has kept
you hitherto. Do you
but hold fast to His
dear hand, and He will
lead you safely through
all things; and, when
you cannot stand, He
will bear you in His
arms.*

—FRANCIS DE SALES,
French saint and bishop
of Geneva

2 Chronicles he wrote of historical events he had not experienced. But for the events of this book, he was a participant. As you read and study, notice the "eyewitness" feel of the book of Ezra.

Although the two parts of the book are separated by fifty-eight years, the theme of rebuilding remains the same throughout. God's chosen people returned to rebuild their homeland. Zerubbabel, in the face of significant challenges, rebuilt the temple. Ezra, in the face of significant sin, rebuilt the people. The work of each complemented the other. A temple of God was needed for the people of God to worship properly. And a people committed to God would be needed for the temple of God to function properly. Each man did his job well. Worship and holiness were restored.

As you read the book of Ezra, look for these concepts:

- Building and rebuilding

- The role of the hand of God

- The prominence of the Word of God

Ezra was written around 2,500 years ago in a faraway land to a unique people in a very different time. Even so, as you read this week, you may see that rebuilding or restoration is needed in your own life as well. Take a few moments to ask God to make you receptive to anything He may want to show you.

? how did the people know who was a real prophet?

MEMORY VERSE

For Ezra had set his heart to study the law of the LORD and to practice it, and to teach His statutes and ordinances in Israel.

EZRA 7:10

REVIEW IT!
The theme of Ezra is rebuilding the home place.

EZRA
[Rebuilding the Temple]

NOTE
The book of Ezra mentions seven different kings and three different world empires.

DAY TWO

COMPLETE READ: Chapters 3–4
QUICK READ: Chapter 1

A CRUCIAL CHAPTER

Sometimes it's difficult to detect the workings of God in our lives and in history. Certain things happen or don't happen. Some we label bad; some we label good. And life keeps moving, sometimes so quickly that we lack the time or insight to search for God in it. Whatever the reason, God often goes unnoticed as the prime mover behind all of life.

But that is not the case in Ezra 1. This chapter is notable for its clarity about what God is doing in the lives of His people. Look through this Crucial Chapter again and write down what you observe God doing and what you observe others doing.

God

Stirred the hearts of Ezra

Others

Our life is full of brokenness—broken relationships, broken promises, broken expectations. How can we live with that brokenness without becoming bitter and resentful except by returning again and again to God's faithful presence in our lives?

—HENRI NOUWEN, twentieth-century priest and author

The episode described in this chapter is *the* impetus behind the exiles beginning their homeward journey. And there is no doubt who initiated it: "The LORD stirred up the spirit of Cyrus king of Persia" (1:1). King Cyrus had just overthrown Babylonia, where the Jews were in exile, and in his first year as ruler he ordered the exiles to pack up, go home, and rebuild the temple of the God who had stirred up his spirit.

We have no idea how God moved Cyrus to this action, but it was bound to happen. Two centuries earlier, Isaiah, a prophet of God, had said that it would. Read Isaiah 44:28–45:7 and record any major truths about God that you discover.

prophesied by Jeremiah

Cyrus was God's handpicked deliverer — he had no choice. And Ezra 1:1-4 is the result. Not only did God choose the deliverer; He also chose the timing. Decades before God stirred up the spirit of Cyrus to issue his decree, another of God's prophets had told the exiles in a letter exactly how long they would be in exile. Read Jeremiah 29:10-14 and summarize what you find there.

"When you seek me"
after 70 years in Babylon

FACT
Cyrus's small tomb can still be seen today amid the ruins of Pasargadae, just north of the Persian Gulf.

The gem cannot be polished without friction, nor man perfected without trials.
—Chinese proverb

Believers in God delight to trace the work of His hand. In this notable chapter, His influence is readily apparent — with plenty of supporting evidence. But it isn't always that clear, is it? How do you typically respond when you are pretty sure that God is involved, but you can't cite enough evidence to remove all doubt?

Read the quote in the margin by Carlo Carretto. Ask God to help you distinguish His sovereign, guiding presence in your own life.

REVIEW IT!
Chapter 1 of Ezra is a Crucial Chapter because of its clarity about the workings of God.

MEMORY VERSE

For Ezra had set his heart to study the law of the LORD and to practice it, and to teach His statutes and ordinances in Israel.

EZRA 7:10

E ZRA
[Rebuilding the Temple]

DAY THREE

COMPLETE READ: Chapters 5–6
QUICK READ: Chapter 3

FACT
Zerubbabel was
included in the line of
the Messiah (see
Matthew 1:12-13).

A PROMINENT PLAYER

Unsung heroes. Unnoticed, they do great things. Behind the scenes they save the day. They quietly and faithfully serve another — or they lead on the front lines of a great cause without fanfare or recognition. Eleanor Roosevelt was an unsung hero. Working behind the scenes for her president-husband FDR, her valuable contribution and faithful service to his administration was incalculable. Following his death, she became a leader in significant humanitarian efforts. In both roles, she was generally "unsung."

Speak of the book of Ezra and we think of . . . Ezra. Think of building projects for the returning exiles and we remember Nehemiah and the walls. But who remembers Zerubbabel, an unsung hero? Maybe it's because we can't spell his name or even pronounce it! Maybe it's because we've simply overlooked him. But read the book of Ezra attentively and you will see the crucial role our Prominent Player filled.

For starters, he led a group of almost fifty thousand returning exiles on a long and tiring trek — over nine hundred miles from Babylonia to Jerusalem. Then he oversaw the rebuilding of the temple in spite of serious opposition from local enemies — serious enough to shut down the project for fifteen years! But when the opportunity to continue building came, he rallied the troops and completed the temple. Without the work of Zerubbabel, Ezra wouldn't have had a house of God as the focal point of his priestly ministry.

The thing that tells in the long run for God and men is the steady persevering work in the unseen. It is inbred in us that we have to do exceptional things for God; but we have not. We have to be exceptional in the ordinary things. It does require the supernatural grace of God to live an ordinary, unobserved, ignored existence as a disciple of Jesus.

—OSWALD CHAMBERS,
*My Utmost for
His Highest*

Unsung hero Zerubbabel was far more than just a building contractor. Note his actions in Ezra 3:1-6 — even before temple construction began. What do these actions say about Zerubbabel's heart? *That he kept the law of Book of moses despite fear of the people*

The foundation for the temple was completed rather quickly. But Zerubbabel's enemies, not wanting the temple to be built, secured a restraining order from King Artaxerxes, and work ceased. Fifteen years later, God intervened by sending His prophets Haggai and Zechariah to instruct the people to begin work on His house once more. Read Haggai 2:1-4 and Ezra 5:1-2. What do you think motivated Zerubbabel to begin rebuilding, even though it was dangerous to do so?

Prophetess of God helped them

Because of Zerubbabel's faithfulness and quiet courage, the temple was completed (Ezra 6:15). An unsung hero became a Prominent Player.

Do you know any unsung heroes? Write down the names that God brings to mind.

In what ways could you acknowledge and affirm them?

MEMORY VERSE

For Ezra had set his heart to study the law of the LORD and to practice it, and to teach His statutes and ordinances in Israel.

EZRA 7:10

REVIEW IT! Zerubbabel rebuilt the temple and is a Prominent Player in the book of Ezra.

E ZRA
[Rebuilding the Temple]

INSIGHT
Ezra was a direct descendant of Moses' brother, Aaron.

DAY FOUR

COMPLETE READ: Chapters 7–8
QUICK READ: Chapter 7

A NOTABLE FEATURE

In his book *The Bible Jesus Read*, Philip Yancey writes,

> Like a drumbeat that never stops, in the pages of the Old Testament we hear the consistent message that this world revolves around God, not us. The Hebrews had incessant reminders built into their culture. They dedicated their firstborn livestock and children to God, wore portions of the law on their heads and wrists, posted visible reminders on their doorways, said the word "blessed" a hundred times a day, even wore distinctive hairstyles and sewed tassels on their garments. A devout Jew could barely make it through an hour, much less an entire day, without running smack into some reminder that he or she lived in God's world. Even the Hebrew calendar marked time by events such as the Passover and Day of Atonement, not merely by the harvest cycle and the moon. The world, they believed, is God's property. And human life is "sacred," which simply means that it belongs to God to do with what He wills.[1]

Yancey describes a culture emerging from and centered around the Word of the Lord. The sacred writings of Israel informed all of life. Every deviation from holiness and every exhortation to repentance was based on truth recorded somewhere in those papyri. Every instruction was grounded in who God was and what He desired.

Unless we form the habit of going to the Bible in bright moments as well as in trouble, we cannot fully respond to its consolations because we lack equilibrium between light and darkness.

—HELEN KELLER, American blind and deaf activist, educator, and writer

No one knew this better than Ezra, the scribe/priest. Our memory verse for this week states it clearly: "For Ezra had set his heart to study the law of the LORD and to practice it, and to teach His statutes and ordinances in Israel."

With that as Ezra's life purpose, it is no surprise that a Notable Feature of this book is a liberal sprinkling of phrases such as:

- the law of the Lord
- the work of the Lord
- the words of the God of Israel
- the commandments of the Lord
- the law of Moses

Read the following verses and record your responses to these questions in the chart:

- Who is speaking, or who is referred to?
- What role does the Word, law, or command of the Lord play?
- What is the response?
- How is the Word of the Lord viewed?

JUST A THOUGHT
One tradition suggests that Ezra originated the synagogue, which was so prominent during the time of Jesus.[2]

PASSAGE	SPEAKING	ROLE OF WORD	RESPONSE	WORD VIEWED
1:1				
3:2				
7:6				
7:10				

Through His words we come to know God Himself, His exact will, His way of looking at things, His most intimate desires, His holy countenance.
—CARLO CARRETTO, Italian spiritual writer

PASSAGE	SPEAKING	ROLE OF WORD	RESPONSE	WORD VIEWED
7:21				
7:23				
7:25				
7:26				
9:4				
9:10-15				

In one sentence or phrase, state your impression of the importance of the Word of the Lord in this book.

Today we call the Word of the Lord "the Bible." How does the importance of the Bible in your life compare to the importance placed upon the Word of the Lord in the book of Ezra?

REVIEW IT!
The prominence of the Word of the Lord is a Notable Feature of the book of Ezra.

MEMORY VERSE

For Ezra had set his heart to study the law of the LORD and to practice it, and to teach His statutes and ordinances in Israel.

EZRA 7:10

Ezra
[Rebuilding the Temple]

DAY FIVE

COMPLETE READ: Chapters 9–10
QUICK READ: Chapter 9

REMEMBER
Ezra worked to rebuild
the exiles spiritually.

A TIMELESS PRINCIPLE

In the foreword to *Knowing Scripture*, J. I. Packer writes,

> If I were the devil, one of my first aims would be to stop folk from digging into the Bible. Knowing that it is the Word of God, teaching men to know and love and serve the God of the Word, I should do all I could to surround it with the spiritual equivalent of pits, thorn hedges, and man traps, to frighten people off. . . . At all costs I should want to keep them from using their minds in a disciplined way to get the measure of its message. . . . Were I the devil, taking stock today, I think I might be pleased at the progress I had made.[3]

As we saw earlier, a Notable Feature of Ezra is a reliance upon the Word of the Lord. Throughout history, people who have humbly engaged in the Word of God have deepened their walk with and expanded their knowledge of Him. It's a Timeless Principle of spiritual health. How does Packer's estimation of the centrality of God's Word compare to your own regard for it?

O God, when my faith gets over laden with dust, blow it clean with the wind of your Spirit. When the habits of obedience get stiff and rusty, anoint them with the oil of your Spirit. Restore the enthusiasm of my first love for You and the alacrity of my first obedience to You, in Jesus' name. Amen.

—EUGENE PETERSON,
Praying with the Psalms

DID YOU KNOW?
Some Bible scholars
believe that Ezra wrote
Psalm 119, the longest
chapter in the Bible.[4]

Read the following statements and then honestly evaluate your own Bible reading and study in light of each one.

> This knowledge of Scripture is not intended merely to fill our minds, like an endless list of do's and don'ts. Rather these external words on the pages of Scripture are to be internalized, written on our hearts by the Holy Spirit.[5]

> In our study of the Bible, we need ever to guard against becoming so engrossed in the fascination of the subject that we lose sight of the object. We want to get hold of the big, broad meanings and movements in the wonderful old Book; but unless the meanings get hold of us our study will have failed in its vital objective.[6]

The Bible has much to say in regard to its influence in the lives of those who read, study, and embrace it:

> The law of the LORD is perfect, restoring the soul;
> The testimony of the LORD is sure, making wise the simple.
> The precepts of the LORD are right, rejoicing the heart;
> The commandment of the LORD is pure, enlightening the eyes.
> The fear of the LORD is clean, enduring forever;
> The judgments of the LORD are true; they are righteous altogether.
> They are more desirable than gold, yes, than much fine gold;
> Sweeter also than honey and the drippings of the honeycomb.
> Moreover, by them Your servant is warned;
> In keeping them there is great reward. (Psalm 19:7-11)

O God, forgive me for looking in all the wrong places for refreshment and renewal—I waste so much time trying out the promises of other people. I return to Your promises and find what I need: forgiveness and counsel and command, even in Jesus Christ. Amen.

—EUGENE PETERSON,

> All Scripture is inspired by God and profitable for teaching, for reproof, for correction, for training in righteousness; so that the man of God may be adequate, equipped for every good work. (2 Timothy 3:16-17)

> How blessed are those whose way is blameless,
> Who walk in the law of the LORD.
> How blessed are those who observe His testimonies,
> Who seek Him with all their heart. (Psalm 119:1-2)

How blessed is the man who does not walk in the counsel
 of the wicked,
Nor stand in the path of sinners,
Nor sit in the seat of scoffers!
But his delight is in the law of the Lord,
And in His law he meditates day and night.
He will be like a tree firmly planted by streams of water,
Which yields its fruit in its season
And its leaf does not wither;
And in whatever he does, he prospers. (Psalm 1:1-3)

Which of these passages touches your heart most strongly? Why?

Notice in the last Scripture reading that the psalmist speaks of
nature's seasons and reminds us that not all of them are fruit-
bearing. It is important to remember that our interaction with
God's Word may look different in different seasons. In your
particular season of life, is there a decision you want to make
regarding your personal interaction with the Word of God? If so,
what would that be?

*Father, You have
anticipated everything
that I need and have
given me wise words of
command, instruction,
and comfort to
surround every
circumstance. As I
listen and believe,
accomplish Your will in
me for Jesus' sake.
Amen.*

—EUGENE PETERSON,
Praying with the Psalms

MEMORY VERSE

For Ezra had set his heart to study the law of the
LORD and to practice it, and to teach His
statutes and ordinances in Israel.

EZRA 7:10

E ZRA
[Rebuilding the Temple]

REVIEW

1. The theme of Ezra is _____rebuilding_____ the home place.

2. Chapter 1 of Ezra is a Crucial Chapter because of its clarity about the
_____working_____ of God.

3. _____Zerubbabel_____ rebuilt the temple and is a Prominent
Player in the book of Ezra.

4. The prominence of the _____word_____ of the Lord is a Notable Feature of the book
of Ezra.

5. "For Ezra had set his heart to study the _____Word law_____ of the
LORD and to practice it, and to teach His statutes and ordinances in Israel."

EZRA 7:_10_

Prayers
Charlotte,
Jill / Kevin
Gwen - Gwen's brother
Arlene
Our country

NEHEMIAH

[Rebuilding the Wall]

So the wall was completed. . . . When all our enemies heard

of it . . . they recognized that this work had been

accomplished with the help of our God.

NEHEMIAH 6:15-16

FOUR

NEHEMIAH
[Rebuilding the Wall]

INTRODUCTION

At the writing of Nehemiah, the temple had been rebuilt, but the people living in Jerusalem were in danger from enemy attacks. The wall around the city lay in ruins, and the gates had been burned. A wall would offer protection and reestablish Jerusalem as a strong city. While living in Susa as the king's cupbearer, Nehemiah received news of the shameful condition of Jerusalem. His heart was burdened, and he asked God to open a way for him to return to Jerusalem. God answered his prayer, and Nehemiah led a third remnant back to the land.

Whereas Ezra rebuilt the spiritual life of the people, Nehemiah worked to rebuild the wall around the city and to establish Jerusalem as the spiritual and political center of Judah. Under his leadership and through the power and might of God, the people — in spite of opposition — rebuilt the wall in just fifty-two days.

Once the wall was reestablished, the people themselves needed to be built up in their devotion to God. Nehemiah joined Ezra and together they worked to establish a civil government and nurture a spiritual people. The book of Nehemiah completes the history of Israel in the Old Testament. All the books that follow fit historically into these first sixteen books.

Nehemiah
[Rebuilding the Wall]

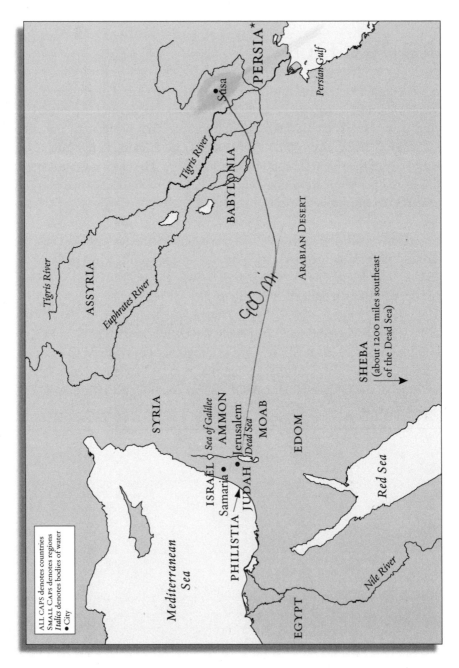

*In the book of Nehemiah, most of the area on this map was under the control of the Persian empire.

NEHEMIAH
[Rebuilding the Wall]

OVERVIEW

WHO: Author: Either Nehemiah or Ezra, using Nehemiah's memoirs (according to most conservative scholars)

WHAT: The rebuilding of the walls of Jerusalem, led by Nehemiah

WHEN: Takes place during the third return of the exiles (445–425 BC)

WHERE: Begins in Susa, Persia, but takes place primarily in Jerusalem, Israel

WHY: Provides background information for the post-exilic period and the prophets and demonstrates the faithfulness of God

I. REBUILDING OF THE WALL: CONSTRUCTION (NEHEMIAH 1–7)

   A. Nehemiah was _Prepared_ by God in captivity.

     1. He was educated in the courts of Persia.

     2. He was a trained leader and organizer of men.

     3. He was the cupbearer to the king.

   B. Nehemiah was a man of _prayer_ .

   C. Nehemiah overcame big _problems_ with the help of our God.

     1. He gave Nehemiah favor in the eyes of the king.

     2. He provided the supplies, the safe travel, and the people that were needed to rebuild.

   D. Nehemiah took a census of all the _people_ who returned.
        ~ 50,000

II. REBUILDING OF THE PEOPLE: INSTRUCTION (NEHEMIAH 8–13)

   A. Ezra _preached_ God's Word to the people.

     1. The people were _convicted_ because they realized how far they were from God's Law.

2. The people _celebrated_ the Feast of the Tabernacles.

3. After a time of _confession_ and prayer, the people signed a _covenant_ .

B. Nehemiah had the people cast lots to determine who would _populate_ the city.

C. Nehemiah and Ezra led the people in dedicating the wall twelve years after its completion.

D. Nehemiah had to return to Jerusalem when the people suffered a spiritual and _political_ relapse.

→ 40 yrs later

APPLICATION

Lives built on the Word of God are less likely to crumble. Do what is POSSIBLE and trust God for the IMPOSSIBLE.

NEHEMIAH
[Rebuilding the Wall]

LEARNING FOR LIFE

1. Beginning with 1 Chronicles, build the foundation for the book of Nehemiah.

2. What was Nehemiah's main mission? How well do you think he accomplished it? Why?

3. How did Nehemiah face challenges, opposition, and fear? Give examples that support your answer.

4. What impressed you the most about Nehemiah?

5. What is God calling you to build in His kingdom?

6. What similarities do you see between Jesus and Nehemiah? (Hint: Think of mission, reliance on God, and identification with the plight of others.)

7. What is the most important thing you learned today? How can you practically apply it to your life?

NEHEMIAH
[Rebuilding the Wall]

INSIGHT
If Ezra wrote this book, he may have used Nehemiah's personal memoirs.

DAY ONE

COMPLETE READ: Chapters 1–3
QUICK READ: Chapters 1–3

THE BIG PICTURE

Have you ever received a phone call that instantly changed your life — either for better or for worse? Have you ever had a conversation that suddenly altered your plans for some time to come? Or received a letter with news of a tragedy or a wonderful event that seemed to mark your life forever? These are life-changing moments. No matter when they happen or how they come to us, when they arrive we understand that our future will not be what we had supposed.

Nehemiah's life-changing moment came as an answer to an innocent question. In 445 BC, Artaxerxes was king of Persia and Nehemiah was his cupbearer — seemingly content and successful in his important position. A group of Persian Jews, including Nehemiah's brother Hanani, had visited Jerusalem and returned to Susa. Interested in his homeland, Nehemiah asked this returning group how things were going there. The answer he was given stunned him: "The remnant there in the province who survived the captivity are in great distress and reproach, and the wall of Jerusalem is broken down and its gates are burned with fire" (Nehemiah 1:3). Upon hearing this news, Nehemiah wept for days and began to fast and pray to God.

As you read the rest of the book, you will see that this encounter drastically changed the future course of Nehemiah's life. He left his position as cupbearer to the king and became a builder of the wall. He left Susa and moved to Jerusalem. He

Our experiences with abandonment and unwanted change are crisis moments when we must decide whether or not to leave behind the life that is gone forever. We can do that only if we believe in the ongoing creativity of God, who brings light and beauty to the dark chaos of our losses in life.

—CRAIG BARNES,
When God Interrupts

left the lap of luxury to work amid the rubble of a city.

The book of Nehemiah continues the record of rebuilding endeavors that began in the book of Ezra. Zerubbabel had rebuilt the temple. Ezra was rebuilding the people. And now Nehemiah would return to Jerusalem to rebuild the wall. This is the theme of this book. To refresh your mind on the chronology of this rebuilding process, review the time line included in Day One of your Ezra study.

The following chart shows the major divisions of the book of Nehemiah:

1 2	7	8 12:26
Preparing to Rebuild the Wall	Genealogy as a Transition	Preparing to Dedicate the Wall
Rebuilding the Wall		Dedicating the Wall
3 6		12:27 13

As you can see, less than half the book covers the actual rebuilding program. Nehemiah 6:15 reads, "So the wall was completed on the twenty-fifth of the month Elul, in fifty-two days." But then a long process of preparing to dedicate the wall began. Ezra joined with Nehemiah to challenge the people spiritually, encouraging their consecration to God and their commitment to continue in His ways. The last half of the book contains a number of stirring religious and spiritual events.

According to Nehemiah 13:6-7, Nehemiah remained in Jerusalem for twelve years before returning to serve King Artaxerxes. But shortly thereafter, he returned again to Jerusalem only to find that the people's commitment to God had severely waned. The book ends with Nehemiah's further efforts at spiritual reform.

All great changes are irksome to the human mind, especially those which are attended with great dangers and uncertain effects.

—JOHN ADAMS, second U.S. president, teacher, and lawyer

As you read Nehemiah, pay close attention to:

- The heart of Nehemiah
- The prominence of prayer
- The expressions of confession

This book has the potential to minister to you in many different ways. How do you think God might use the story of Nehemiah to speak to your heart and life?

Pray and ask God to soften your heart so that any seed He may want to plant there will find ready soil.

Memory Verse

So the wall was completed.... When all our enemies heard of it ... they recognized that this work had been accomplished with the help of our God.

Nehemiah 6:15-16

REVIEW IT!
The theme of Nehemiah is rebuilding the wall.

NEHEMIAH
[Rebuilding the Wall]

DAY TWO

COMPLETE READ: Chapters 4–6
QUICK READ: Chapter 1

INSIGHT
Less than 10 percent of
Nehemiah's chapter 1
prayer focuses on his
request.

A CRUCIAL CHAPTER

The first chapter of a book isn't often the most Crucial Chapter, but it certainly is in the book of Nehemiah. Trying to understand this book without understanding chapter 1 leaves a reader with unanswered questions and confusion. This chapter introduces the players and their attitudes, as well as the extent of the problems they faced.

Nehemiah 1:2-3 is a capsule outline of the entire book. The following chart shows that Nehemiah asked Hanani two questions in verse 2. Fill in the answers he received from his brother in verse 3.

1:2	**1:3**
Question #1: "concerning the Jews"	Answer #1: *They are in great distress and under reproach.*
Question #2: "about Jerusalem"	Answer #2: *The wall has been breached and the gates have been gutted w/ fire.*

I am only one, but still I am one. I cannot do everything, but still I can do something; and because I cannot do everything, I will not refuse to do something that I can do.
—EDWARD EVERETT HALE, nineteenth-century American author and clergyman

INTERESTING!
Nehemiah confessed
his own sin and those
of others in his prayer
in chapter 1.

Compare this chart to the chart that follows and you will see that these two questions and their answers contain in a nutshell the two parts of the book. The first question and answer point to the rebuilding of the people recorded in chapters 8–13, and the second question and answer foreshadow the rebuilding of the wall recorded in chapters 2–6.

Question About Jerusalem		Question About the Jews
Answer: Wall Down	Chapter 7	Answer: Great Distress
Chapters 2–6		Chapters 8–13
Rebuild the Wall		Rebuild the People

When Nehemiah received the distressing news about Jerusalem and its people, he was cupbearer to King Artaxerxes, nine hundred miles removed from Jerusalem. A cupbearer was one of the top officials of the king's court. It was his special duty to serve wine to the king in his royal wine cup. Because of the prevalence of political enemies, the cupbearer would pour a small quantity and swallow it to show that the drink was not poisoned.

Our main business is not to see what lies dimly at a distance, but to do what lies clearly at hand.

—Thomas Carlyle, Scottish essayist and historian of the nineteenth century

If the cup was poisoned, no more cupbearer, but long live the king! Because of the cupbearer's responsibilities to the king, a deep intimacy and trust developed between these two men. Nehemiah was a man of importance and a man of station. He was probably not a man looking for something else to do!

When Nehemiah received the answers to his questions, he could have responded in many different ways: "My, I am so sorry to hear that" or "Why doesn't someone over there do something about the situation?" or "Well, I guess we're just getting what we deserve." But that wasn't Nehemiah's heart, so that's not how he responded. His response is recorded in 1:4-11. As you read and think through these verses, write down your answers to the following questions.

What was his response to the news he received?

he wept and mourned. Then he fasted + prayed.

What was surprising about his response?

The depth of his feeling + that he felt like he needed to go there himself.

What does this response indicate about Nehemiah?

How much he cared also he remembered the promise God gave moses - if you return to me + keep the commandments, - I will gather

What does this response teach us about God?

your people and bring them back to the place I have chosen as the dwelling place for my name.

Chapter 1 of Nehemiah sets the stage for the rest of the book. It opens our eyes to the problems that needed to be addressed. And, perhaps more important, it opens our eyes to the heart of the man who would address those problems.

What challenged you the most in verses 4-11?

Reputation is what men and women think of us. Character is what God and the angels know of us.

—THOMAS PAINE, American patriot and political philosopher

MEMORY VERSE

So the wall was completed.... When all our enemies heard of it ... they recognized that this work had been accomplished with the help of our God.

NEHEMIAH 6:15-16

REVIEW IT!
As our Crucial Chapter, chapter 1 is a capsule and summary of the entire book of Nehemiah.

NEHEMIAH
[Rebuilding the Wall]

INTERESTING!
To be sad in the presence of the king (Nehemiah 2:12) was usually grounds for severe punishment.

DAY THREE

COMPLETE READ: Chapters 7–9
QUICK READ: Chapter 4

A PROMINENT PLAYER

C. S. Lewis, in his book *Mere Christianity,* writes,

> Every time you make a choice you are turning the central part of you . . . into something a little different from what it was before. All your life long you are slowly turning this central thing either into a Heaven creature or into a hellish creature; either into a creature that is in harmony with God, and with other creatures, and with itself, or else into one that is in a state of war and hatred with God, and with its fellow creatures, and with itself. . . . Each of us at each moment is progressing to the one state or the other.[1]

In the book of Nehemiah, we are privy to a relatively thin slice of Nehemiah's life, yet in it we can see the truth of Lewis's statement lived out. This man's responses, choices, and actions were so consistent in this thin slice that we can justifiably assume this consistency was also present throughout his entire life.

Courage is almost a contradiction in terms. It means a strong desire to live taking the form of a readiness to die.

—G. K. CHESTERTON, English author of *Orthodoxy*

The choices our Prominent Player made in the nitty-gritty of practical experience show his consistent dependence on God. In Day Two of this week, you spent time investigating Nehemiah 1:4-11. Look at verse 4 again and specifically state the choice Nehemiah made as you see it. *He took on the sins of his people + was willing to risk the king's wrath to go do the work.*

In chapter 2, the king asked Nehemiah what was bothering him. Nehemiah said it was the plight of Jerusalem, and the king asked him what he would like to request.

What choices do you see Nehemiah make in 2:4-8? What do you think these choices may have built into his character?

Resolve. Hope that he was in God's favor/plan.

Opposition to the wall rebuilding quickly arose from foreigners who did not want to see the city of Jerusalem securely protected. That opposition is described in 4:1-3, and Nehemiah's response to it follows in 4:4-6. Describe Nehemiah's choices in the face of opposition and consider the growth that could have resulted in him personally.

He stationed guards & told the people to keep the Lord in mind.

Nehemiah's second trip to Jerusalem is described in chapter 13. When he arrived, he found evil upon evil being done by the people. In 13:23-31, he aggressively attacked those who had disobeyed God by marrying foreign wives. He even took the powerful and prestigious priesthood to task. What choices do you think Nehemiah had to make in putting an end to this behavior, and how might those choices have strengthened him as a person?

Prob some of these people were his friends. He also tore families apart

The goodness of God knows how to use our disordered wishes and actions, often lovingly turning them to our advantage while always preserving the beauty of His order.

—Saint Bernard of Clairvaux, twelfth-century French abbot of Clairvaux

Many times our choices become the raw material for the fabric of our lives. How have your own choices functioned in your life to develop your godly character?

MEMORY VERSE

So the wall was completed.... When all our enemies heard of it ... they recognized that this work had been accomplished with the help of our God.

NEHEMIAH 6:15-16

REVIEW IT!
Nehemiah is the Prominent Player in this dramatic story.

 NEHEMIAH
[Rebuilding the Wall]

DAY FOUR

COMPLETE READ: Chapters 10–11
QUICK READ: Passages in this day's lesson

A NOTABLE FEATURE

In one of his comics, *Family Circus* artist Bill Keane shows little Billy kneeling on his bed, hands clasped in prayer. His father peeks through the door as Billy says, "Listen to this, God, here's an offer you can't refuse."

Isn't that how we — as kids *and* adults — sometimes view prayer? But in our more mature moments, we know prayer is not some form of sanctified deal making, and we can agree with E. M. Bounds, who writes, "Prayer honors God; it dishonors self. It is man's plea of weakness, ignorance, want. A plea which Heaven cannot disregard. God delights to have us pray."[2]

Have you noticed how prayer was strongly woven through the tapestry of Nehemiah's life and ministry? He prayed often. He prayed widely. And he prayed boldly. But *never* did he try to make a deal with God. Over and over he clearly stated the concerns of his heart, praised God for who He is, and then moved on, trusting that he had engaged in one of life's most significant interactions.

Reflect on the Scripture passages in the following chart and record your thoughts about our Notable Feature, Nehemiah's prayer life, by answering these questions in the chart:

- What was the situation or need?

- What was the tone of the prayer (if the actual prayer is recorded)?

- What was the explicit or implied response of God (if any)?

*Prayer is keeping
company with God.*

—CLEMENT OF
ALEXANDRIA, Greek saint
who lived from
AD 150–220

INSIGHT
Hippocrates, the father
of medicine, was a
contemporary of
Nehemiah.

Passage	Situation/Need	Tone	God's Response
2:1-5			
4:1-6			
4:7-15			
5:19; 13:14,22,31			
6:8-9			
6:12-14; 13:28-29			

Prayer enlarges the heart until it is capable of containing God's gift of Himself.

—MOTHER TERESA, twentieth-century Indian humanitarian, missionary, and religious leader

Linking your thoughts from this study with those from Day Two about Nehemiah's prayer in 1:5-11, compose a short description of Nehemiah as a man of prayer.

What one thing about today's study challenged or encouraged you the most?

MEMORY VERSE

So the wall was completed. . . . When all our enemies heard of it . . . they recognized that this work had been accomplished with the help of our God.

NEHEMIAH 6:15-16

REVIEW IT!
Prayer is the Notable Feature of Nehemiah, and Nehemiah was a man of prayer.

NEHEMIAH
[Rebuilding the Wall]

REFLECT
Almost 60 percent of the content in chapters 8–10 describes the people's confession of sin, illustrating the importance of confession to them and to God.

DAY FIVE

COMPLETE READ: Chapters 12–13
QUICK READ: Chapter 9:1-8,32-38

A TIMELESS PRINCIPLE

Prayer is the soul's sincere desire, uttered or unexpressed;
The motion of a hidden fire that trembles in the breast.

No prayer is made on earth alone, the Holy Spirit pleads;
and Jesus on the eternal throne for sinners intercedes.

O Thou by Whom we come to God, the Life, the Truth,
the Way,
the path of prayer Thyself hast trod: Lord, teach us how
to pray.

—JAMES MONTGOMERY, "PRAYER IS THE
SOUL'S SINCERE DESIRE"[3]

If ever a principle is *timeless*, it is the principle of the all-encompassing necessity of prayer. And if ever a principle is *timely*, it is the principle of the all-encompassing necessity of prayer. We are busy people — but so was Nehemiah. We are distracted and stressed people — but so was Nehemiah. And like Nehemiah, we are needy and helpless. Prayer was Nehemiah's avenue to strength and wisdom and patience and peace. And it can be ours as well. Prayer is a Timeless Principle.

In his book *Prayer: Finding the Heart's True Home*, Richard Foster writes,

> For too long we have been in a far country: a country of noise and hurry and crowds, a country of climb and push

That prayer has a great power which a person makes with all his might. . . . It draws down the great God into the little heart; it drives the hungry soul up into the fullness of God; it brings together two lovers, God and the soul, in a wondrous place where they speak much of love.

—MECHTILD OF MAGDEBURG, thirteenth-century mystic writer

and shove, a country of frustration and fear and intimidation. And he welcomes us home: home to serenity and peace and joy, home to friendship and fellowship and openness, home to intimacy and acceptance and affirmation.

We do not need to be shy. He invites us into the living room of his heart, where we can put on old slippers and share freely. He invites us into the kitchen of his friendship, where chatter and banter mix in good fun. He invites us into the dining room of his strength, where we can feast to our heart's delight. He invites us into the study of his wisdom, where we can learn and grow and stretch . . . and ask all the questions we want. He invites us into the workshop of his creativity, where we can be co-laborers with him, working together to determine the outcomes of events. He invites us into the bedroom of his rest, where new peace is found and where we can be naked and vulnerable and free. It is also the place of deepest intimacy, where we know and are known to the fullest.[4]

How would you describe your present level of intimacy with God in these various rooms of His being?

Helplessness becomes prayer the moment that you go to Jesus and speak candidly and confidently with him about your needs.

—O. HALLESBY, *Prayer*

Despite God's desire for us to draw near to Him in prayer, our human tendency to take action sometimes causes us to perceive prayer as idle or lazy, as James Gilman explains,

My creed leads me to think that prayer is efficacious, and surely a day's asking God to overrule all events for good is not lost. Still there is a great feeling that when a man [woman] is praying he is doing nothing, and this feeling makes us give undue importance to work, sometimes even to the hurrying over or even to the neglect of prayer.[5]

Do you ever feel that praying is "doing nothing"? Take time to write a prayer to God expressing this frustration. If you do not experience difficulty in prayer, how would you encourage someone who does?

In Nehemiah's prayers, you saw great simplicity and honesty. Sometimes we attempt to be "deep" and to hide our true thoughts and feelings from God. But He is perfectly willing and able to hear anything we utter, wise or unwise. God has heard it all before — just check out the book of Psalms! C. S. Lewis counsels those of us who pray to "lay before Him what is in us, not what ought to be in us."[6]

What do you need to lay before God that you may have been hiding or perhaps watering down? Will you do it now?

We, too, become tired, deadly tired! Then it is blessed to know of a place where we can lay our tired head and heart, our heavenly Father's arms, and say to Him "I can do no more. And I have nothing to tell You. May I lie here a while and rest? Everything will soon be well again if I can only rest in Your arms a while."

—O. HALLESBY, *Prayer*

What is your greatest desire for your prayer life?

MEMORY VERSE

So the wall was completed.... When all our enemies heard of it ... they recognized that this work had been accomplished with the help of our God.

NEHEMIAH 6:15-16

NEHEMIAH
[Rebuilding the Wall]

REVIEW

1. The theme of Nehemiah is _rebuilding_ the wall.

2. As our Crucial Chapter, chapter 1 is a capsule and _summary_ of the entire book of Nehemiah.

3. _Nehemiah_ is the Prominent Player in this dramatic story.

4. _Prayer_ is the Notable Feature of Nehemiah, and Nehemiah was a man of prayer.

5. "So the _wall_ was completed. . . . When all our enemies heard of it . . . they recognized that this work had been accomplished with the help of our God."

NEHEMIAH 6:_____ - _____

ESTHER

[Exiles' Providential Protection]

And who knows whether you have not attained

royalty for such a time as this?

Esther 4:14

Five

Feb 23
- Yay- Judy's son's house sold.
  Rachel safety.
- Angie's niece doing better
  Gwen injection back.

ESTHER
[Exiles' Providential Protection]

INTRODUCTION

Between chapters 6 and 7 in the book of Ezra, there is a fifty-eight-year gap. The book of Esther takes place during this historical period and is the only book that gives a glimpse of court life in Persia. Though thousands of Jews returned to Jerusalem after the Exile, several million chose to remain behind in Persia.

The book of Esther is unusual because the name of God is never mentioned, and yet the story clearly demonstrates the hand of God directing events, protecting His children, and judging the wicked. As evil Haman devised a plan to completely annihilate the Jewish population in Persia, Mordecai approached his cousin, Esther, for help. Though Esther was a Jew, she had been chosen to be queen by the Persian king, Ahasuerus.

It is this courageous young woman who stepped forward and risked her life for the Jewish people. Through a series of divinely orchestrated events, she was able to unveil Haman's wicked plot and persuade the king to stop it. Esther's story is full of twists and turns, but in the end the people were saved. This historic event is still celebrated by Jews everywhere and is called the Feast of Purim.

ESTHER
[Exiles' Providential Protection]

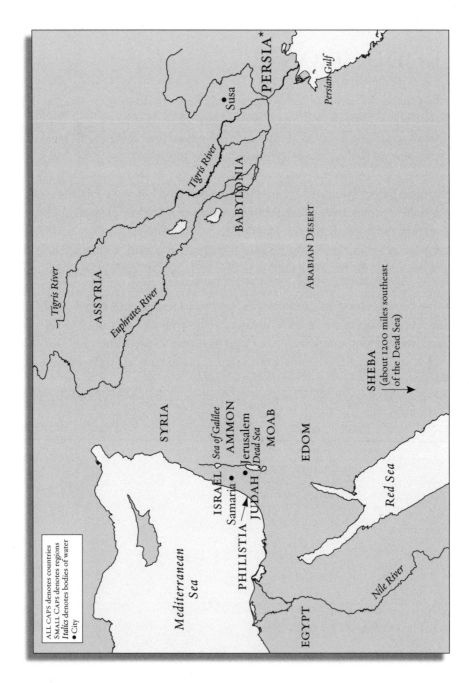

*In the book of Esther, most of the area on this map was under the control of the Persian empire.

ESTHER
[Exiles' Providential Protection]

OVERVIEW

WHO: Author: Unknown
Main Characters: Ahasuerus, king of Persia; Haman, his prime minister; Mordecai; Esther; the Jews remaining in Persia

WHAT: The exiles are protected

WHEN: 483–473 BC; during the 60 years between the Jews' first return to Canaan led by Zerubbabel and the second return led by Ezra

WHERE: Persia

WHY: To show how God's hidden hand works behind the scenes to protect His people

I. PLOTS OF MEN (CRISIS ANTICIPATED) (ESTHER 1–5)

A. Ahasuerus was the _King_ of Persia.

    1. Vashti, the queen, refused the king's command.

    2. The king banished _Vashti_ from the palace.

B. _Esther_ was crowned as Persia's new queen.

C. Mordecai, Esther's ~~uncle~~ _cousin_, saved the king's life.

D. Haman, the Agagite, was promoted over all the princes.

    1. Mordecai, the Jew, refused to _bow_ to Haman.

    2. Haman sought to destroy all the _Jews_ .

II. THE PROTECTION OF GOD (CRISIS AVERTED) (ESTHER 6–10)

A. God's Perfect Timing

    1. God controlled Haman's cast of Pur. The date to destroy the Jews was eleven months in the future.

    2. Mordecai commanded Esther to be an _advocate_ for the Jews.

3. Esther delayed advocating for the Jews until the second banquet. Haman built gallows to _kill_ Mordecai.

4. King Ahasuerus, unable to _sleep_, read how Mordecai saved his life.

5. Haman arrived at the exact time the king desired Mordecai honored.

B. God's People Protected

1. Esther exposed Haman's plot at the second banquet.

2. Haman was _killed_ on gallows he prepared for Mordecai.

3. Mordecai replaced the irrevocable decree with a new one: The Jews can defend themselves.

4. The Feast of Purim was established to remember and celebrate God's hidden hand of _protection_.

APPLICATION

When God's voice can't be heard, His hand can be seen. God is at work behind the scenes, protecting His people. He uses people to accomplish His plan, and His timing is always perfect.

Abraham
Jacob — Esah → grandson Emalech

Haman was: Agagite descendeur of king of Malachites, enemy of the Jews

ESTHER
[Exiles' Providential Protection]

LEARNING FOR LIFE

1. Where geographically does the book of Esther take place? What was happening to God's people at that time? Persia / Susn

2. Describe how Esther became queen. How do you see the plots of men and the protection of God at work in her attaining this position?

3. Describe Haman's plot. Who did he hate and why? Mordecai refused to bow to him

4. What are some examples of God's perfect timing in this story? What does this say about your own life?

5. Give specific illustrations of how God's hidden hand protected His people from their enemy, Haman.

6. Can you share an example of a time God's hidden hand of protection was evident in your own life?

7. How is Jesus our advocate? (Hint: See Hebrews 4:14-16 and 1 John 2:1.)

8. What did you learn about God today? How did He personally encourage or correct you?

ESTHER
[Exiles' Providential Protection]

DAY ONE

COMPLETE READ: Chapters 1–2
QUICK READ: Chapters 1–2

THE BIG PICTURE

In his book *Reaching for the Invisible God*, Philip Yancey writes,

> In high school, I took pride in my ability to play chess. I joined the chess club, and during lunch hour could be found sitting at a table with other nerds poring over books with titles like *Classic Pawn Openings*. I studied techniques, won most of my matches, and put the game aside for 20 years. Then, in Chicago, I met a truly fine chess player who had been perfecting his skills long since high school. When we played a few matches, I learned what it is like to play against a master. Any classic offense I tried, he countered with a classic defense. If I turned to more risky, unorthodox techniques, he incorporated my bold forays into his winning strategies. Although I had complete freedom to make any move I wished, I soon reached the conclusion that none of my strategies mattered very much. His superior skill guaranteed that my purposes inevitably ended up serving his own.... When a Grand Master plays a chess amateur, victory is assured no matter how the board may look at any given moment.[1]

This is certainly the story of the book of Esther. It's a classic struggle between good and evil, between God and Satan, between God's people and their enemies. In move after move and counter move after counter move, the outcome of the game

Spiritual tenacity [means] to work deliberately on the certainty that God is not going to be worsted. One of the greatest strains in life is the strain of waiting for God. Remain spiritually tenacious.

—OSWALD CHAMBERS,
My Utmost for His Highest

seems up for grabs. But in the end, the Grand Master of heaven wins — as He always has, does, and will.

Esther's story contains colorful characters, suspense, irony, and intrigue. And it's full of surprises — the kind that are covered in God's fingerprints.

The story takes place in the years 483–473 BC between the returns of Zerubbabel and Ezra. (For a reminder, refer to the timeline in the Ezra Day One study.) King Ahasuerus (Xerxes) of Persia deposed his queen, Vashti, and then held a "Miss Persia" beauty contest to find her replacement. Esther, a Jewess, was chosen, and the intrigue began.

Queen Esther had been raised by her cousin, Mordecai, a loyal Jew who feared God and believed that God alone was worthy of honor and worship. Mordecai refused to bow down to Haman, the king's prime minister, and Haman became infuriated. He convinced the king to issue a decree declaring that on an appointed day in the future, the native Persians would rise up and kill all the Jews remaining in Persia. Mordecai and Esther conspired to foil the planned bloodbath, and a complex and dramatic plot unfolded.

The chart that follows gives an overview of this exciting book.

1 5	6 10
Crisis ANTICIPATED	Crisis AVERTED
HAMAN Preeminent	MORDECAI Preeminent
Esther as QUEEN to Ahasuerus	Esther as SAVIOR to her people
God's PREPARATION	God's PRESERVATION

The author of Esther is unknown, but the abundance of detail and obvious understanding of Persian life has led scholars to believe that its writer was an eyewitness to the events described. It was likely written to encourage the Jewish exiles who had not returned to Jerusalem with Zerubbabel. The message is clear:

FACT
Something written into the law of the Medes and Persians could not even be changed by the king (Esther 1:19).

God speaks to every individual through what happens to them moment by moment. The events of each moment are stamped with the will of God. If we have abandoned ourselves to God, there is only one rule for us: the duty of the present moment.

—JEAN-PIERRE DE CAUSSADE, eighteenth-century Jesuit priest

God is still our God, and in His sovereignty He will care for us.

As you read the book, watch for the theme — the hidden hand of God — as the events transpire.

What events in chapters 1 and 2 interested or intrigued you the most?

wondering why Esther was acceprable Queen if she was a Jew / not asked for her lineage?

MEMORY VERSE

And who knows whether you have not attained royalty for such a time as this?

ESTHER 4:14

ESTHER: DAY ONE

ESTHER
[Exiles' Providential Protection]

DAY TWO

COMPLETE READ: Chapters 3–5
QUICK READ: Chapters 3–5

A CRUCIAL CHAPTER

In the game of chess, all moves are important and together lead to either victory or defeat. But at times, a move or series of moves becomes especially weighty, drastically affecting the eventual outcome of the game. In that sense, chapter 5 is a Crucial Chapter in the book of Esther. It contains three specific, behind-the-scenes moves by God in the lives of three different characters: Ahasuerus, Esther, and Haman.

Xerxes

MOVE NUMBER 1
Gaining entrance into the king's presence was not a simple thing. One never knew if the king would grant an audience or not — and if he refused, he owed no one an explanation. Anyone entering his court *without* being summoned was putting his life in jeopardy.

The background to move number 1 is in Esther 4:10-17. Read verses 10-11 and briefly describe the situation in your own words.

DID YOU KNOW?
The golden scepter was always the same height as the king.

There are three things that only God knows: the beginning of things, the cause of things, and the end of things.
—Welsh proverb

WOW!
In today's currency,
Haman would have
offered nearly $20
million to kill off the
Jews (Esther 3:9).

Now read verses 12-17. What does Mordecai's challenge to
Esther and Esther's response to Mordecai say about each of
them as people?

*She respected & honored him. He expec
her to do for her people, remembering
she was a Jew and that perhaps
there was a reason why she was
in the position she was in*

Move number 1 happens in chapter 5. Read verses 1-2. What
do you think was going on in Esther's mind and heart as she
waited? What might she have felt after God moved Ahasuerus
to extend the golden scepter and accept her?

Relief obviously, plus trepidation.

Move Number 2

At Esther's banquet prepared for the king and Haman, God
needed a divine postponement. He put it in Esther's mind to
cause the "Great 24-Hour Delay." This delay became extremely
pivotal to God's plan. Read 6:1-10 and in your own words
describe the significance of God influencing Esther to create a
24-hour delay.

*God is the master of
the scenes; we must
not choose what part
we shall act; it
concerns us only to be
careful that we do it
well, always saying, "If
this please God, let it
be as it is."*

—Jeremy Taylor,
seventeenth-century
Anglican minister

Move Number 3

In 5:9-14 Haman was both elated and angered.

What elated him?

~~beauty~~
power
~~bragging~~

What angered him?

~~drink~~
~~not~~ doing as he asked

What alleviated his anger?

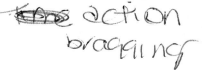
~~his~~ action
bragging

God's move to cause Haman to build a gallows to hang Mordecai led to the irony of ironies in the ensuing drama! Read 7:8-10.

The Grand Master of heaven cannot be outwitted or outplayed. He not only uses the moves of His people but also the moves of His enemies as part of His overall strategy for bringing about the results He desires.

Ask God to show you some of His behind-the-scenes moves in your life and to build your faith as your eyes are opened more and more.

Memory Verse

> And who knows whether you have not attained royalty for such a time as this?
>
> ESTHER 4:14

God comes at last when we think he is furthest off.

—English proverb

REVIEW IT!
Chapter 5 is our Crucial Chapter because of three behind-the-scenes moves by God.

FACT
Esther is one of two books in the Bible named for a woman. (The other is Ruth.)

ESTHER
[Exiles' Providential Protection]

DAY THREE

COMPLETE READ: Chapters 6–7
QUICK READ: Chapters 6–7

A PROMINENT PLAYER

Have you ever been in *just* the right place at *just* the right time? And did you know it? If you have been and you did know, then you certainly experienced the satisfaction and enjoyment of that moment! But so often we're in the right place at the right time and we have no idea. It may be days, weeks, or even years before the importance of our "right place-right time" moment is revealed to us.

Earlier in biblical history, Joseph was imprisoned in Egypt (see Genesis 40). Pharaoh's cupbearer was thrown into prison, and Joseph — a trusted prisoner — had charge over him. When the cupbearer had a strange dream, Joseph interpreted it for him, and later the cupbearer was released and reinstated to serve Pharaoh. *Two years later* when Pharaoh had a strange dream demanding interpretation, the cupbearer remembered Joseph. Joseph interpreted Pharaoh's dream, was released from prison, and rose to second in command of all Egypt. Joseph had certainly been in the right place at the right time two years earlier, but it took those two years for the impact of his "right place-right time" moment to be revealed.

The same thing happened in the life of Mordecai, a Prominent Player in the amazing drama of Esther. He was in just the right place at just the right time — not by chance, but by God's sovereign design. Yet the complete impact of his "right place-right time" moment wouldn't be fully revealed until later in the story.

In the Divine purposes, before the Lord created the heavens and the earth, God loved His own people. He had chosen you, thought of you, provided for you and made the thousand forecasts of loving kindness towards you before the earth was.

—CHARLES SPURGEON, nineteenth-century British preacher

The author introduces Mordecai in Esther 2:5 as a Jew and a Benjamite. He was also a cousin of Esther. When Esther's father and mother (Mordecai's uncle and aunt) died, he accepted responsibility for her and "took her as his own daughter" (2:7). In time, Esther was selected for the king's harem. What does 2:11 indicate about Mordecai?

he was a good familyman

The "right place-right time" moment in Mordecai's life took place in 2:19-23. Describe in your own words what happened.

he happened to be @the gate when Esther passed

INSIGHT
Mordecai's letters in Esther 8:10 were probably delivered by the fastest horses in the empire.

Chapter 3 details Mordecai's refusal to bow down to Haman, Haman's anger at this outright affront, and his decree to kill all of the Jews in the land because of the snub of one Jew. Mordecai heard about the decree, and his response is recorded in 4:1. What does this tell you about Mordecai?

he felt bad for his people

Mordecai again played a major role in 4:13-17. Review what you wrote about him concerning this incident on Day Two of this study.

Almighty God, who always moves with clarity of will and singleness of purpose, help me to live and work with certainty in an uncertain world. Light a lamp before me so that my feet do not stumble. Make my path clear so I may never wander from Your chosen way. I pray in the name of Jesus who comes to make Your way clear before our eyes. Amen.

—Christian prayer

The crucial nature of the incident in 2:19-23 finally becomes apparent in 6:1-14. If you have not yet read 6:1-14 for this lesson, read it now. Notice and revel in the sovereign irony of God as He works all things according to His — and not man's — plan.

From this point on, Mordecai's status drastically changed. He received the signet ring that belonged to Haman, was given authority to issue a counterdecree to Haman's murderous one, and was outfitted in "royal robes of blue and white, with a large crown of gold and a garment of fine linen and purple" (8:15). Chapters 9:3-4 and 10:2-3 summarize the place to which he had risen in the kingdom. Briefly describe what these verses reveal about Mordecai.

Review what you've learned about Mordecai and write a brief appraisal.

What qualities did he model that you would like to emulate?

REVIEW IT!
Mordecai is our Prominent Player because of his role in the ultimate ironic event in the drama.

MEMORY VERSE

And who knows whether you have not attained royalty for such a time as this?

ESTHER 4:14

ESTHER
[Exiles' Providential Protection]

DAY FOUR

COMPLETE READ: Chapter 8
QUICK READ: Chapter 8

REMEMBER
A king's sleepless night
changed everything!

A NOTABLE FEATURE

The book of Esther has a Notable Feature that no other book of the Bible can claim. Have you noticed it? God is *never* mentioned! Not once. And yet, when one views the book from the proper perspective, His presence permeates the drama.

High in the Andes Mountains of Peru lies a flat plain thirty-seven miles long with roads and paths that go nowhere. Crisscrossing at random, these strange lines were thought by archaeologists to be an ancient road network emerging from the centuries-old city of Nazca. Where they led or what sense to make of their random design escaped all observers on the ground.

Quite a different perspective is gained from the air, however. From ten thousand feet, it is startlingly clear that these lines are not roads at all, but part of a vast desert mural of amazing proportion, depicting objects that are many miles in height. What the murals are and how, for whom, and why they were built are all lost in the mystery of the past. But they do teach us a valuable lesson: Often the whole picture of something cannot be seen if we are too close to it.

The mysterious is always attractive. People will always follow a veil.
—BEDE JARRETT, popular English Dominican preacher

This is true of the book of Esther. If we focus on the details of the story, never stepping back far enough to get the big picture, we will see it only as a tension-filled drama of human choices and actions. But when we catch the bigger, broader perspective, we realize that the individual details are too odd, too ironic, and too well-timed to be just human life living itself out. This story has

AMAZING!
According to Josephus, a Jewish historian of the first century, Esther was chosen queen from among four hundred candidates.

too much divine glue holding it together to be interpreted as good luck, chance, or happenstance. God is not mentioned — but He was always present. The hidden hand of God was working to carry out His plan and fulfill His desires.

Go back and review just a few of the many incidents that show the hidden hand of God. Read each of the following verses and briefly describe God's work behind the scenes.

2:7 Mordecai adopted Esther She was beautiful

2:21 Mordecai was in the right place @ the right time.

6:1 King unable to sleep heard story of Mordecai

6:4 Haman happened to be in the court to see if he could ger favor to hang Mordecai

All work that is worth anything is done in faith.

—ALBERT SCHWEITZER, winner of the Nobel Peace Prize in 1952

Clearly the participants of the Esther drama recognized the importance of the phenomenal deliverance from death that

God had accomplished for them. Read 9:20-28 and briefly describe what they established as a means of remembering.

The Feast of Purim is celebrated even today at its established time two days during the month of Adar, which corresponds to our February–March. On the evening of the first day the people gather together to read the book of Esther, and when Haman's name is read, they shout in unison, "Let his name be blotted out!" The children participate with noisemakers and Purim rattles. On the second day, after a formal religious service in the morning, they devote themselves to rejoicing — using hymns, plays, dramas, and recitations. In remembrance of Esther 9:19, they also send food and gifts to the poor.[2]

The impact of God's hidden hand was not lost on the Jews. They recognized it — and celebrated it.

Are there some "hidden" works of God that you have recognized in your life? If so, have you found some way to celebrate them? If not, what might you do to honor His intervention?

MEMORY VERSE

And who knows whether you have not attained royalty for such a time as this?

ESTHER 4:14

REVIEW IT!
The Notable Feature of the book of Esther is that the name of God is never mentioned.

E STHER

[Exiles' Providential Protection]

SCARY STUFF!
King Ahasuerus ordered
a bridge built over the
Hellespont, but when it
was later destroyed in a
storm, he ordered that
three hundred strokes
of the scourge be
inflicted on the sea and
the builders beheaded.

DAY FIVE

COMPLETE READ: Chapters 9–10
QUICK READ: Chapters 9–10

A TIMELESS PRINCIPLE

> Behind the dim unknown stands God within
> the shadows keeping watch over His own.
>
> —ANONYMOUS

At times, God seems to stand in the shadows. But given a chance,
wouldn't we much rather experience Him standing in the light?
We feel more confident when we can see Him clearly, assured
that everything will work out for good. But if the book of Esther
teaches us anything, it is that sometimes God works incognito —
though just as mightily as ever — with His providence concealed.
God's unseen hand at work is a Timeless Principle.

Describe a time in your life when God seemed to be invisible.

*We both believe, and
disbelieve a hundred
times an Hour, which
keeps Believing nimble.*

—EMILY DICKINSON,
nineteenth-century
American poet

Philip Yancey, in his book *Reaching for the Invisible God,* writes,

> Isaiah said it bluntly: "Truly you are a God who hides him-
> self." In a meditation on this verse, Belden C. Lane
> remarks that he used to fret about how his children played

hide-and-seek. His son would bellow out "Ready!" when he found a good hiding place, which of course instantly gave him away. Lane, the father, kept reviewing the point of the game — "You're supposed to hide, not give your position away!" — until one day it dawned on him that from his son's perspective he had missed the point of the game. The fun comes in being found, after all. Who wants to be left alone, undiscovered?

"God is like a person who clears his throat while hiding and so gives himself away," said Meister Eckhart.[3]

Often God does clear His throat, letting us know He is there and working. And when He does we feel better. Confident and secure. At peace.

Describe a time in your life when God clearly demonstrated His presence.

But there are also times when God doesn't make a sound, when He is painfully silent. No doubt Esther and Mordecai knew the silence of God and found themselves thirsty for evidence of God's work on their behalf.

Yancey goes on,

My own understanding of God's hiddenness traces back not to the childhood game of hide-and-seek but rather to my first visit to a natural history museum. I gawked at the huge stuffed grizzly bears and the woolly mammoths and the yellowed skeletons of whales and dinosaurs hanging from the ceiling. One exhibit, however, kept beckoning

FACT
Esther was a Jew who married a Gentile. Ruth was a Gentile who married a Jew.

Get these principles fixed in your hearts: that things eternal are much more considerable than things temporal; that things not seen are as certain as the things that are seen.
—JOHN WESLEY, author of *Classics of Western Spirituality*

Proverbs 26:1 fits
Haman perfectly:
"Honor is not fitting for
a fool."

me: a display of animal camouflage. When I first walked past it, I saw side-by-side scenes of winter and summer foliage. Only when I returned and stared intently did I notice the animals hiding in the diorama: a ferret chasing a snowshoe hare in the winter scene, praying mantises, birds, and moths in the summer. A placard detailed how many animals were hidden, and I spent half the day lingering there, trying to locate them all.[4]

Lingering might be a good response when God seems hidden, camouflaged. That's what we have begun to do in the book of Esther. We have lingered, searched, and endured until the God who is never mentioned by name becomes visible in the shadows.

Describe your response when God has seemed camouflaged in your life.

What would it be like for you to linger, to search, to endure until the eyes of your heart begin to see His presence in the shadows?

A religion without mystery must be a religion without God.
—JEREMY TAYLOR, author and professor

If you are having trouble finding Him, it might help to pray this prayer of A. W. Tozer:

Oh God and Father, . . . Thou hast been here and I knew it not. I have been blind to Thy Presence. Open my eyes that I may behold Thee in and around me. For Christ's sake, Amen.[5]

But no matter how hard we look and listen, there are times in life when God remains hidden. Often we think it is failure on our part — that we must not have tried hard enough. But we have to understand that silence and mystery are part of the nature of God. And it is in those times that we must trust what we cannot see — His faithfulness — and hope for what we cannot feel — His mercy. Even in the darkness, we can rest in His love.

God comes like the sun in the morning — when it is time. We must assume an attitude of waiting, accepting the fact that we are creatures and not Creator. The initiative is God's, not ours. We are able to initiate nothing; we are able only to accept.

—CARLO CARRETTO, The God Who Comes

MEMORY VERSE

And who knows whether you have not attained royalty for such a time as this?

ESTHER 4:14

ESTHER
[Exiles' Providential Protection]

REVIEW

1. The theme of Esther is the _____hidden_____ hand of God.

2. Chapter 5 is our Crucial Chapter because of three behind-the-_____scenes_____ moves by God.

3. _____Mordecai_____ is our Prominent Player because of his role in the ultimate ironic event in the drama.

4. The Notable Feature of the book of Esther is that the name of _____God_____ is never mentioned.

5. "And who knows whether you have not attained royalty for such a _____time_____ as this?"

ESTHER 4:_14_

COMPREHENSIVE REVIEW OF
THE POST-EXILIC BOOKS

1 CHRONICLES

1. The theme of 1 Chronicles is _____ for the temple.

2. Our Notable Feature Number 1 is the _____ and their hidden treasures.

3. Because of their encouragement to David, our Prominent Players are _____ mighty men.

4. Our Notable Feature Number 2 is _____ joyful acceptance of God's ministry for him.

5. "Yours, O LORD, is the greatness and the power and the glory and the victory and the majesty, indeed _____ that is in the heavens and the earth; Yours is the dominion, O LORD, and You exalt Yourself as head over all."

1 CHRONICLES 29:_____

2 CHRONICLES

1. The theme of 2 Chronicles is _____ the temple.

2. _____ is a Prominent Player in 2 Chronicles.

3. A Crucial Chapter in 2 Chronicles is chapter 12 in which _____ forsakes God.

4. A Notable Feature of 2 Chronicles is the occurrence of periodic _____ .

5. "For the eyes of the LORD move to and fro throughout the earth that He may strongly support those whose _____ is completely His."

2 CHRONICLES 16:_____

EZRA

1. The theme of Ezra is _____ the home place.

2. Chapter 1 of Ezra is a Crucial Chapter because of its clarity about the
_____ of God.

3. _____ rebuilt the temple and is a Prominent
Player in the book of Ezra.

4. The prominence of the _____ of the Lord is a Notable Feature of the book of Ezra.

5. "For Ezra had set his heart to study the _____ of the
LORD and to practice it, and to teach His statutes and ordinances in Israel."

EZRA 7:_____

NEHEMIAH

1. The theme of Nehemiah is _____ the wall.

2. As our Crucial Chapter, chapter 1 is a capsule and _____
of the entire book of Nehemiah.

3. _____ is the Prominent Player in this dramatic story.

4. _____ is the Notable Feature of Nehemiah, and
Nehemiah was a man of prayer.

5. "So the _____ was completed. . . . When all our enemies heard of
it . . . they recognized that this work had been accomplished with the help of our God."

NEHEMIAH 6:_____-_____

ESTHER

1. The theme of Esther is the _____ hand of God.

2. Chapter 5 is our Crucial Chapter because of three behind-the-_____
moves by God.

3. _____ is our Prominent Player because of his role in the ultimate ironic event in the drama.

4. The Notable Feature of the book of Esther is that the name of _____ is never mentioned.

5. "And who knows whether you have not attained royalty for such a _____ as this?"

ESTHER 4:_____

CONGRATULATIONS!

You have just completed The Post-Exilic Books, set three of *The Amazing Collection: The Bible for Women, Book by Book*. Our travels have been extensive since we left the Garden of Eden back in Genesis. In these history books, we have journeyed to Ur, Canaan, Egypt, Mount Sinai, the wilderness, and back to Canaan (renamed Israel); we've been exiled to Babylonia and have finally returned to Jerusalem. The Historical Books have covered about four thousand years. At the end of Nehemiah, the recorded Old Testament history came to an end. The next twenty-two Old Testament books contain both poetry and prophecy and fit into the historical timeline of the first three sets.

The people of Israel may have been on the move, but God was empowering them all the while with music, poetry, drama, and literature. The next five books are a sampling of Jewish literature, but in reality they are the work and inspiration of God. All five books are considered poetry, yet they utilize different forms. Job and Song of Solomon are dramatic poems that tell a story. Proverbs and Ecclesiastes are didactic in nature as they instruct. Psalms was written to be accompanied by musical instruments and sung in worship.

As with every book in the Bible, these books paint exquisite pictures of our God and Savior. He is sovereign. He is beauty. He is all-wise. He is our lover. He is our all.

As we prepare to move on to these beautiful literary treasures, get ready for your heart to be expanded by God's great majesty . . . and get ready to kneel in worship and awe.

So now, let the adventure continue with set four, The Poetical Books of *The Amazing Collection*.

CHRONOLOGICAL RELATIONSHIP OF
THE OLD TESTAMENT BOOKS

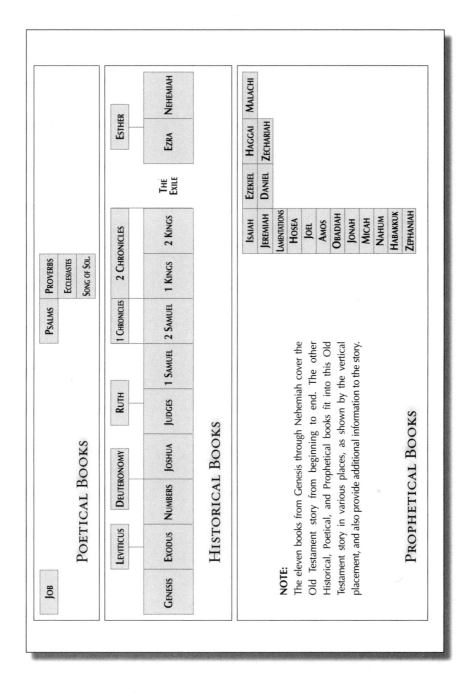

POETICAL BOOKS

JOB

PSALMS | PROVERBS | ECCLESIASTES | SONG OF SOL.

HISTORICAL BOOKS

GENESIS | EXODUS | LEVITICUS | NUMBERS | DEUTERONOMY | JOSHUA | JUDGES | RUTH | 1 SAMUEL | 2 SAMUEL | 1 KINGS | 2 KINGS

1 CHRONICLES | 2 CHRONICLES

THE EXILE

ESTHER | EZRA | NEHEMIAH

PROPHETICAL BOOKS

ISAIAH | EZEKIEL | HAGGAI | MALACHI
JEREMIAH | DANIEL | ZECHARIAH
LAMENTATIONS
HOSEA
JOEL
AMOS
OBADIAH
JONAH
MICAH
NAHUM
HABAKKUK
ZEPHANIAH

NOTE:

The eleven books from Genesis through Nehemiah cover the Old Testament story from beginning to end. The other Historical, Poetical, and Prophetical books fit into this Old Testament story in various places, as shown by the vertical placement, and also provide additional information to the story.

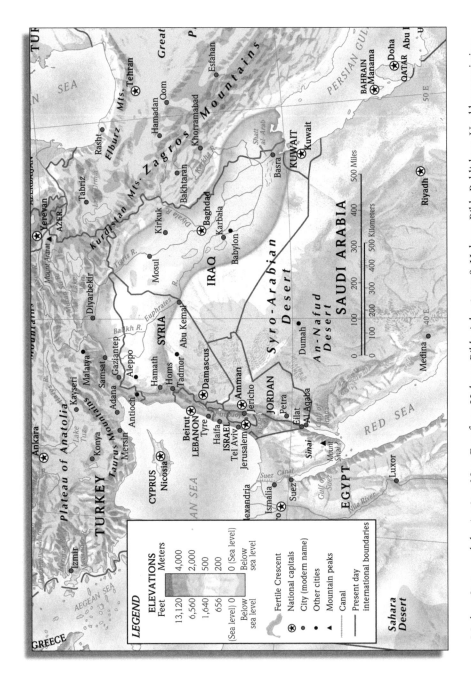

Modern States and the Ancient Near East from Holman Bible Atlas © 1998, Holman Bible Publishers. Used by permission.

Jewish Exiles in Babylonia

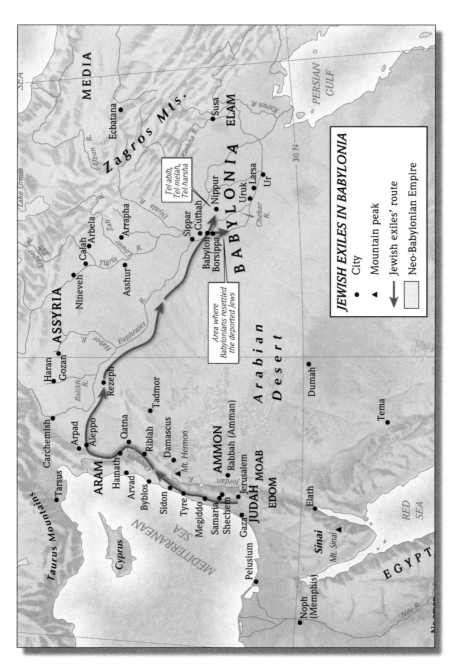

Jewish Exiles in Babylonia from Holman Bible Atlas © 1998, Holman Bible Publishers. Used by permission.

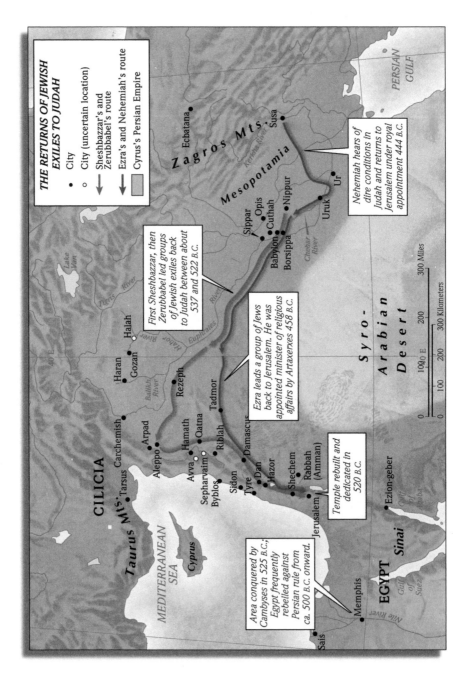

THE RETURNS OF JEWISH EXILES TO JUDAH
- City
- City (uncertain location)
- Sheshbazzar's and Zerubbabel's route
- Ezra's and Nehemiah's route
- Cyrus's Persian Empire

First Sheshbazzar, then Zerubbabel led groups of Jewish exiles back to Judah between about 537 and 522 B.C.

Ezra leads a group of Jews back to Jerusalem. He was appointed minister of religious affairs by Artaxerxes 458 B.C.

Nehemiah hears of dire conditions in Judah and returns to Jerusalem under royal appointment 444 B.C.

Temple rebuilt and dedicated in 520 B.C.

Area conquered by Cambyses in 525 B.C.; Egypt frequently rebelled against Persian rule from ca. 500 B.C. onward.

PERSIAN GULF

Ecbatana · Zagros Mts. · Susa

Kerkha River

Mesopotamia

Sippar · Opis · Cuthah · Nippur · Uruk · Ur
Babylon · Borsippa
Chebar River

Lake Van

Tigris River · Euphrates River · Habor River · Balikh River

Halah · Haran · Gozan · Rezeph · Tadmor · Damascus

Syro-Arabian Desert

100 E · 100 · 200
0 · 100 · 200 · 300 Miles
0 · 100 · 200 · 300 Kilometers

40 E

CILICIA
Taurus Mts. · Tarsus · Carchemish · Arpad · Aleppo · Hamath · Qatna · Riblah
Avva · Sepharvaim · Byblos · Sidon · Tyre · Dan · Hazor · Shechem · Rabbah (Amman)
Jerusalem

MEDITERRANEAN SEA

Cyprus

EGYPT · Sinai
Memphis · Sais
Nile River · Gulf of Suez · Gulf of Aqaba · Ezion-geber

Return of the Jewish Exiles from Holman Bible Atlas © 1998, Holman Bible Publishers. Used by permission.

ANSWER KEY TO OUTLINES

1 CHRONICLES

I. GENEALOGIES (1 CHRONICLES 1–9)

A. God traced the genealogy of Judah's twenty-one <u>KINGS</u> from King David to the Exile.

B. God traced the genealogy of the Levites.

1. All Levites were to <u>SERVE</u> in the temple.

2. Some Levites, Aaron's sons, were the priests.

II. DAVID'S REIGN — PREPARING TO BUILD THE TEMPLE (1 CHRONICLES 10–29)

A. David prepared the place.

1. David captured the city of <u>JERUSALEM</u>.

2. David returned the <u>ARK</u> to Jerusalem.

B. David repeated the promise.

1. David's son <u>SOLOMON</u> would build the temple.

C. David prepared the provisions.

1. David used spoils of battles as building materials.

2. David bought land for the temple <u>SITE</u>.

D. David prepared the people.

1. David prepared the builders.

2. David prepared the Levites and priests.

3. David prepared himself to DIE.

    a. David declared Solomon king.

    b. David prepared Solomon to build.

    c. David prepared the people to give.

    d. David WORSHIPED God.

    e. David prayed for the people.

2 CHRONICLES

I. THE NATION OF ISRAEL IN ITS GLORY: LOOK TO THE PAST (2 CHRONICLES 1–9)

A. King Solomon received WISDOM from God.

B. Solomon built the temple and it symbolized the PRESENCE of God in the nation.

    1. It took seven years to build the temple.

    2. All of the stones were cut off-site.

    3. The temple was built on Mount Moriah.

    4. The temple was built with cedar, silver, bronze, and gold.

    5. The temple contained no idols.

    6. There was only one temple in Israel because there was only one God.

    7. The temple was thirty feet by ninety feet and forty-five feet high.

    8. The temple had only two interior rooms.

    9. Only the priests entered the temple.

C. The nation of Israel enjoyed PEACE, prosperity, and prestige under Solomon's rule.

II. THE NATION OF JUDAH IN ITS DECLINE AND DESTRUCTION: LEARN FOR THE PRESENT (2 CHRONICLES 10)

A. There were twenty kings in Judah.

1. There were EIGHT good kings in Judah and twelve evil kings.

a. AHAZ was an example of an evil king.

b. HEZEKIAH was an example of a good king.

2. There were five revivals recorded in 2 Chronicles.

B. Jerusalem and the temple were destroyed by Babylon in 586 BC.

C. Many of the people were taken into EXILE to Babylon.

III. THE NATION YET TO BE: LIVE FOR THE FUTURE (2 CHRONICLES 36)

A. Jeremiah (29:10) had prophesied before the fall of Jerusalem that the people would return from exile after seventy years.

B. God chose Cyrus, king of Persia, to allow the people to go back to Judah to rebuild the temple.

EZRA

I. FIRST RETURN: REMNANT REBUILT (EZRA 1–6)

A. Released Remnant — Fulfillment of Prophecy (Ezra 1–2)

1. The people were given two choices: RETURN or SUPPORT the return.

2. A CENSUS was taken to number the returning remnant.

B. Rebuilding Began (Ezra 3)

1. ZERUBBABEL was God's choice to lead the remnant home.

2. The people PRAYED to God because they were motivated by FEAR.

3. Protected by God, the FOUNDATION was laid.

C. Restoration Hindered by Opposition (Ezra 4)

1. The enemy's first tactic was COMPROMISE.

2. The second tactic employed was <u>DISCOURAGEMENT</u>.

3. The third tactic used was <u>ACCUSATION</u>.

D. Remnant Rallied by Prophets (Ezra 5)

E. Rebuilding of Temple Completed (Ezra 6)

II. SECOND RETURN: REMNANT REVIVED (EZRA 7–10)

A. Readied for Return Under Ezra (Ezra 7–8)

1. The return began as <u>EZRA</u> found favor with the king and the people were allowed to leave.

2. The remnant was counted and prepared through prayer and returned safely to Israel.

B. Recognition of Sin by Ezra (Ezra 9)

1. Reports of <u>UNFAITHFULNESS</u> reached Ezra.

2. <u>REBELLION</u> of the people grieved Ezra. He mourned as the fearful people were summoned.

C. Renewal of Covenant (Ezra 10)

1. <u>RESTORATION</u> of Israel's relationship with God began.

2. <u>REPENTANCE</u> brought revival.

NEHEMIAH

I. REBUILDING OF THE WALL: CONSTRUCTION (NEHEMIAH 1–7)

A. Nehemiah was <u>PREPARED</u> by God in captivity.

1. He was educated in the courts of Persia.

2. He was a trained leader and organizer of men.

3. He was the cupbearer to the king.

B. Nehemiah was a man of <u>PRAYER</u>.

C. Nehemiah overcame big <u>PROBLEMS</u> with the help of our God.

1. He gave Nehemiah favor in the eyes of the king.

2. He provided the supplies, the safe travel, and the people that were needed to rebuild.

D. Nehemiah took a census of all the PEOPLE who returned.

II. REBUILDING OF THE PEOPLE: INSTRUCTION (NEHEMIAH 8–13)

A. Ezra PREACHED God's Word to the people.

1. The people were CONVICTED because they realized how far they were from God's Law.

2. The people CELEBRATED the Feast of the Tabernacles.

3. After a time of CONFESSION and prayer, the people signed a COVENANT.

B. Nehemiah had the people cast lots to determine who would POPULATE the city.

C. Nehemiah and Ezra led the people in dedicating the wall twelve years after its completion.

D. Nehemiah had to return to Jerusalem when the people suffered a spiritual and POLITICAL relapse.

ESTHER

I. PLOTS OF MEN (CRISIS ANTICIPATED) (ESTHER 1–5)

A. Ahasuerus was the KING of Persia.

1. Vashti, the queen, refused the king's command.

2. The king banished VASHTI from the palace.

B. ESTHER was crowned as Persia's new queen.

C. Mordecai, Esther's COUSIN, saved the king's life.

D. Haman, the Agagite, was promoted over all the princes.

1. Mordecai, the Jew, refused to BOW to Haman.

2. Haman sought to destroy all the JEWS.

II. THE PROTECTION OF GOD (CRISIS AVERTED) (ESTHER 6–10)

A. God's Perfect Timing

1. God controlled Haman's cast of Pur. The date to destroy the Jews was eleven months in the future.

2. Mordecai commanded Esther to be an <u>ADVOCATE</u> for the Jews.

3. Esther delayed advocating for the Jews until the second banquet. Haman built gallows to <u>KILL</u> Mordecai.

4. King Ahasuerus, unable to <u>SLEEP</u>, read how Mordecai saved his life.

5. Haman arrived at the exact time the king desired Mordecai honored.

B. God's People Protected

1. Esther exposed Haman's plot at the second banquet.

2. Haman was <u>KILLED</u> on gallows he prepared for Mordecai.

3. Mordecai replaced the irrevocable decree with a new one: The Jews can defend themselves.

4. The Feast of Purim was established to remember and celebrate God's hidden hand of <u>PROTECTION</u>.

NOTES

1 CHRONICLES
1. *Stories for the Heart*, comp. Alice Gray (Sisters, Oreg.: Multnomah, 1996), p. 105.

2 CHRONICLES
1. *Stories for the Heart*, comp. Alice Gray (Sisters, Oreg.: Multnomah, 1996), p. 108.

2. A. W. Tozer, *Pursuit of God* (Harrisburg, Pa.: Christian Publications, Inc., 1948), p. 72.

3. Tozer, p. 59.

4. Saint Bernard, quoted in Tozer, p. 15.

5. Tozer, p. 65.

EZRA
1. Philip Yancey, *The Bible Jesus Read* (Grand Rapids, Mich.: Zondervan, 1999), p. 28.

2. *Zondervan Pictorial Encyclopedia of the Bible*, vol. 5 (Grand Rapids, Mich.: Zondervan, 1975), pp. 555-556.

3. J. I. Packer, foreword to *Knowing Scripture*, by R. C. Sproul (Downers Grove, Ill.: InterVarsity, 1977), pp. 9-10.

4. L. A. T. Van Dooren, *Introducing the Old Testament* (Grand Rapids, Mich.: Zondervan, 1967), p. 91.

5. Jack Kuhatschek, *Applying the Bible* (Downers Grove, Ill.: InterVarsity, 1990), p. 25.

6. J. Sidlow Baxter, *Explore the Book*, vol. 1 (Grand Rapids, Mich.: Zondervan, 1960), p. 12.

NEHEMIAH
1. C. S. Lewis, *Mere Christianity*, 10th ed. (New York: The MacMillan Company, 1969), p. 86.

2. E. M. Bounds, *Purpose in Prayer* (Chicago: Moody), p. 41.

3. James Montgomery, *Hymns for the Family of God* (Nashville, Tenn.: Paragon Associates, Inc., 1976), p. 446.

4. Richard J. Foster, *Prayer: Finding the Heart's True Home* (New York: HarperSanFrancisco, 1992), pp. 1-2. Reprinted by permission of HarperCollins Publishers Inc.

5. James Gilman cited in Bounds, p. 5.

6. C. S. Lewis, *Letters to Malcolm: Chiefly on Prayer* (New York: Harcourt, Brace & World, 1964), p. 22.

ESTHER

1. Philip D. Yancey, *Reaching for the Invisible God* (Grand Rapids, Mich.: Zondervan, 2000), pp. 262-263. Used by permission of The Zondervan Corporation.

2. Robert Jamieson, *Critical and Experimental Commentary, Volume II: Joshua—Esther* (Grand Rapids, Mich.: Eerdmans, 1967), p. 649.

3. Yancey, p. 116. Used by permission of The Zondervan Corporation.

4. Yancey, p. 118. Used by permission of The Zondervan Corporation.

5. A. W. Tozer, *Pursuit of God* (Harrisburg, Pa.: Christian Publications, Inc., 1948), p. 72.

LEADER'S GUIDE

1. *Webster's New Collegiate Dictionary* (Springfield, Mass.: G&C Merriam Co. Publishers, 1960), p. 237.

2. John K. Brilhart, *Effective Group Discussion* (Dubuque, Iowa: Wm. C. Brown Company Publishers, 1967), p. 26.

3. *How to Lead Small Group Bible Studies* (Colorado Springs, Colo.: NavPress, 1982), pp. 40-42.

BIOGRAPHIES

PAT HARLEY
Teacher

Pat committed her life to Jesus Christ at the age of thirty-two after He powerfully intervened and healed her broken marriage. After eight years of study, she began teaching the Bible to women, convinced that it is the Word of God that offers help and hope for women today. She is the founder and president of Big Dream Ministries, Inc. and served for eighteen years as the director of The Women's Fellowship, a former ministry to over five hundred women. She also served as the director of women's ministries at Fellowship Bible Church in Roswell, Georgia. Pat has a master of arts degree in education from Western Michigan University and has taken courses at Dallas Theological Seminary. She and her husband have two married daughters and several grandchildren.

ELEANOR LEWIS
Teacher

At the age of twenty-six, Eleanor accepted Christ for assurance of heaven. However, when her son was born with a severe birth defect, she turned to God's Word for answers and found not only a Savior but an all-powerful Lord. The Word of God came alive for her, and she began teaching and speaking at Christian women's clubs. For almost thirty years, she has taught Bible studies in churches, homes, and offices. In addition, she speaks at conferences and retreats across the country and internationally. She is president of Insights and Beginnings, Inc., which produced a video series and Bible study to help people understand their temperament types, overcome weaknesses, and use their strengths for the glory of God. Eleanor and her husband live in the Atlanta area and have a married son and one grandchild.

MARGIE RUETHER
Teacher

Though Margie was not raised in a churchgoing home, her parents committed their lives to Christ after Margie was in college. It was her mother's godly example and prayers that brought Margie to the throne of grace. Her growing love for Jesus and His Word led her to Bible Study Fellowship International, an interdenominational Christian organization in which laypeople teach Bible studies. After many years of study, she became a Substitute Teaching Leader and a member of the area team. She served there for a number of years before becoming one of the lead teachers at The Women's Fellowship in Roswell, Georgia. She has also facilitated a Bible teacher-training program for women and speaks at retreats and church conferences. She and her family live in Delaware.

LINDA SWEENEY
Teacher

Linda accepted Christ as her personal Savior when she was twelve years old. As an adult, she grew to love God's Word more and more. She began to see God change not only her life but the lives of others when they adhere to the wisdom of Scripture. Because of her passion to excite women to know the Word and to see their lives change as they respond in obedience, she began teaching the Bible to women in her church and community under God's leading. She has taught Sunday school for many years and was a much-loved Bible Study Fellowship International Teaching Leader for eight years. During that time, she not only taught hundreds of women weekly but also trained a large group of Bible Study Fellowship International leaders in her class. She has taught women's retreats and spoken at women's meetings and conferences throughout the South. She and her husband live in the Atlanta area and have a married daughter, a son, and two grandchildren.

ART VANDER VEEN
Senior Copywriter

Art began his relationship with Christ at age thirteen. In his late twenties after graduating from the University of New Mexico, he began preparing for full-time ministry. He earned a Th.M. degree from Dallas Theological Seminary and has ministered on the staff of Campus Crusade for Christ. He was one of the original team members of Walk Thru the Bible Ministries and served as chaplain for the Atlanta Falcons. In 1979, he was part of a team that founded Fellowship Bible Church in Roswell, Georgia, where he was a pastor for nearly twenty-five years. He now serves as pastor, teacher, and mentor at Little Branch Community Church in the Atlanta area. Art is passionate about helping people understand the Scriptures as the revealed truth from and about God. He and his wife, Jan, have three married children and seven grandchildren.

CARRIE OTT
Editor, Designer

Carrie met Christ at an early age. All her life she has had a passion for words, and as a freelance writer and designer, this passion doubles when it is words — seen, read, and grasped — that attempt to sketch a portrait of the mystery and wonder of God and His Word. Carrie identifies with Mechtild of Magdeburg, who said, "Of the heavenly things God has shown me, I can speak but a little word, no more than a honeybee can carry away on its foot from an overflowing jar." Carrie and her husband have three children and live in the Atlanta area.

To learn more about
Big Dream Ministries, Inc. and
The Amazing Collection,
visit their website at:

www.theamazingcollection.org

LEADER'S GUIDE

INTRODUCTION

Leading a group Bible study can be a challenging but incredibly rewarding experience. This Leader's Guide will provide help with the "challenging" part, as you trust God to produce the "incredibly rewarding" piece.

This guide is not designed to take you step-by-step through the individual studies. Instead, it will offer some general guidance and instruction in principles and techniques. Most of what you learn here will not be specific to *The Amazing Collection* but applicable to many kinds of group study. The one exception is Appendix B.

Each section of this Leader's Guide will deal with a single subject, making it easier for you to return to the guide for future help and reference.

Thank you for accepting the challenge and responsibility of leading your group! We pray God will make this a rewarding and profitable experience for you.

DISCUSSION: THE ESSENTIAL COMPONENT

The words *small-group Bible study* are almost synonymous with the term *discussion*. While there are very significant places and purposes for lecturing (one-way communication), for the most part a small group is not one of them. Therefore, discussion is an essential component of a successful small-group experience.

Discussion is the investigation of a subject or question by two or more people using verbal dialogue. Webster defines it as "consideration of a question in open debate; argument for the sake of arriving at truth or clearing up difficulties." Additionally, the word *discuss* and its synonyms mean "to discourse about so as to reach conclusions or to convince. Discuss also implies a sifting or examining, especially by presenting considerations pro and con."[1]

Small-group Bible studies will not always include debate or argument, but there *should* always be investigation, examination, and the reaching of at least tentative conclusions.

There are many benefits to discussion-style learning compared to lectures or even to interaction that is dominated by one person. Discussion:

- Keeps every member more involved in the learning process
- Allows for self-disclosure, enabling the participants to get to know each other better
- Helps crystallize the thinking of each group member by creating a venue in which topics can be investigated at deeper levels
- Creates a more informal atmosphere, which encourages a sense of relaxed learning
- Provides the potential of uncovering misconceptions and correcting misinformation
- Fosters more permanent learning and change because people tend to better remember what is said rather than what is thought
- Builds a sense of community as participants cooperate in their search for truth and understanding

While small-group Bible studies that foster healthy discussion will realize the above benefits, the depth of any group experience is greatly enhanced by an able leader. The leader plays an important role in helping each of these seven benefits become reality. For example, in order to keep every member more involved in the learning process, the leader will need to encourage those who tend to hide and manage those who tend to dominate. The other benefits require similar sensitivity by the leader. The remainder of this guide is intended to help the leader maximize these benefits for her small group.

But before we move on, one more issue should be addressed. While the leader is a crucial player in a small group, he or she should not become the person to whom all other participants address their remarks. One author has suggested that a discussion leader should strive to foster an "all-channel" network, rather than become the "hub" or center of a discussion wheel, as the following diagrams depict.

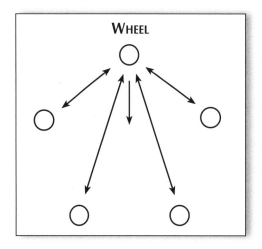

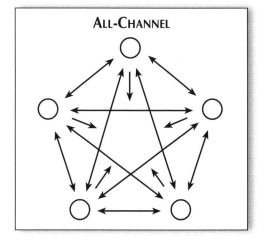

In a "wheel" network, all comments are directed toward one central leader, and he or she alone speaks to the group as a whole or to any one person.

By contrast, an "all-channel" network allows rapid communication without requiring clearance from a central gatekeeper; everyone is free to share thoughts that come to mind while they are still relevant to the topic at hand. Free exchange of questions and responses is thus encouraged.[2]

The leader's responsibility is to continually remember the need for "all-channel" communication.

LISTENING: THE LOST ART

You've probably heard it said that God gave us two ears and one mouth because He wanted us to listen twice as much as we talk. It would be difficult to prove that assumption, but the Bible *does* say:

> But everyone must be quick to hear, slow to speak. (James 1:19)

> He who gives an answer before he hears,
> It is folly and shame to him. (Proverbs 18:13)

Listening may be the most powerful tool of a successful small-group leader, but it is also possibly the most difficult trait to develop. Most people tend to talk more than listen, be more concerned about their interests than the interests of others, and listen impatiently, hoping the other person will finish quickly. True listening is a lost art, which a good small-group leader must recapture.

Listening is not just hearing. As reading is to seeing, listening is to hearing. By both reading and listening, we understand the real meaning of the words our senses "take in."

Consider the following ideas and use them to evaluate your own listening habits and skills. Then, decide which areas you could intentionally improve.

Listening Characteristics:
- It is active, not passive, and therefore sometimes tiring.

- It is other-centered, not self-centered, and therefore sometimes sacrificial.

- It is crucial, not peripheral, and therefore indispensable.

- It is difficult, not easy, and therefore often neglected.

- It is scarce, not common, and therefore greatly desirable.

Listening is not *like:*

- A chess game — planning your next verbal move while the other person is talking

- A trial — judging what is said or how it is said

- A 100-yard dash — thinking how quickly you can end the discussion

Listening is like:

- A sponge — absorbing as much as possible of what is being said and the feelings behind it

- A pair of binoculars — fixing attention on and bringing into clear focus what is being said

Kinds of Questions:

- Information — "What did you do today?"

- Opinion — "Why do you think that happened?"

- Feeling — "How do you feel about that?"

Kinds of Responses:

- Clarification — "I think what you're saying is . . ." This gets at the meaning of what was said.

- Observation — "I noticed that your voice dropped when . . ." This acknowledges the importance of nonverbal cues.

- Reflection — "You seem quite sad about . . ." This acknowledges the emotional component.

- Inquiry — "Tell me more about . . ." This seeks additional information and often gleans further insight.

While you are listening, consider silently praying for wisdom:

- "God, what are you doing in this person's heart right now?"

- "Father, help me to hear what she is really saying."

- "Eternal Counselor, what kind of response do you want me to make to what this person is saying?"

There will be times as a small-group leader when you will need to limit one member's input to allow for total group input. Your aim is not to encourage never-ending dialogue with one person, but to bring the most and the best out of each participant and the group as a whole, maximizing discussion, insight, and impact more fully than you may have thought possible.

QUESTIONS: THE MENTAL CROWBARS

Good questions can spell the difference between success and failure in a small-group setting. As you lead discussions of *The Amazing Collection*, the Learning for Life discussion questions at the beginning of each study will give you an excellent starting point. But there will be times when you will want to probe differently or more deeply. At such times, forming good questions will be incredibly important.

Some of these questions may be prepared ahead of time. Others will be developed as you go. Remember, every good question shares some common characteristics:

- Brief — short and uncluttered
- Applicable — relevant to the people's needs
- Simple — easily understood
- Interesting — capable of holding attention
- Conforming — based on the material being studied

As a leader you may ask launching, guiding, and application questions. The following material describes these three types of questions, giving examples of each.

Launching Questions:

- Initiate meaningful discussion on a subject
- May be prepared ahead of time
- Will determine to a large extent the direction your discussion will take
- Are general questions intended to stimulate discussion
- Must be based on the participants' previous study to enable quality contributions
  Examples:
  - "What did you discover in this passage about . . . ?"
  - "What impressed you most about how God . . . ?"
  - "What thoughts do you have about Moses after this study?"
  - "Why do you think God included this passage in the Bible?"
  - "How would you describe the holiness of God?"

Guiding Questions:

- Keep the discussion moving, drawing out the most important ideas and refocusing a wandering discussion
- May be prepared ahead of time as you anticipate the subjects that will be raised by the group

- May be crafted as the discussion is in high gear (This takes practice!)
- Take the participants beyond initial observations and more deeply into the meaning of the material

  Examples:
  - "Sally just mentioned the concept of obedience. How does that fit with what this passage seems to say?"
  - "Who else would like to comment on that?"
  - "We've said a lot of things about grace in our discussion. If you had to boil it down to a sentence, what would you say?"
  - "What we're discussing is interesting, but we've wandered from where we want to go. Can someone take us back to where we veered off the trail?"

Application Questions:
- Are supplied for you in *The Amazing Collection* workbooks
- May be developed based on your own knowledge of the group
- May be difficult to formulate but serve as the bridge from Bible study to daily living — from the head to the heart
- Do not always involve something concrete to do or to change
- Could include meditation, reflection, remembering, or simply waiting on God
- May be questions that will encourage the group to share their answers aloud or may suggest a more private response
- May be specific or general
- Must relate to the truth the group has just studied

  Examples:
  - "Write a prayer pouring out your heart to God in response to what He has been teaching you this week."
  - "Do you know someone who models well what we have just studied? How could you affirm that person this week?"
  - "What do you sense God is asking you to do in response to your study?"
  - "What do you see in this character's life that you would like to imitate? What would that look like? What is the first step?"

Crafting and asking questions are skills that can be developed and honed. After each group meeting, it might be useful to evaluate your questions. Did they lead the group where you sensed God wanted to lead? Which "as you go" guiding questions worked well or not so well? How did the group respond to the questions? Was there any confusion? Finally, make a point to review anything you learned about asking questions each week.

ROLES PEOPLE PLAY: THE ULTIMATE CHALLENGE

If being a small-group Bible study leader involved only facilitating discussion, learning to listen well, and forging meaningful questions, the challenge would be large enough. But add to that the fact that every person in your group will have different needs, temperaments and personalities, approaches to Bible study, reasons for being there, and levels of maturity, and the role of leadership becomes exponentially more challenging.

Professor Howard Hendricks of Dallas Theological Seminary describes in *How to Lead Small Group Bible Studies* some of the roles people play in group situations. You may find these helpful in evaluating your own group's dynamic.

Immature roles

The onlooker	Content to be a silent spectator. Only nods, smiles, and frowns. Other than this, he is a passenger instead of a crew member.
The monopolizer	Brother Chatty. Rambles roughshod over the rest of the conversation with his verbal dexterity. Tenaciously clings to his right to say what he thinks — even without thinking.
The belittler	This is Mr. Gloom. He minimizes the contributions of others. Usually has three good reasons why some opinion is wrong.
The wisecrack	Feels called to a ministry of humor. Mr. Cheerio spends his time as the group playboy. Indifferent to the subject at hand, he is always ready with a clever remark.
The hitchhiker	Never had an original thought in his life. Unwilling to commit himself. Sits on the sidelines until others reach a conclusion, then jumps on the bandwagon.
The pleader	Chronically afflicted with obsessions. Always pleading for some cause or action. Feels led to share this burden frequently. One-track mind.
The sulker	Lives with a resentful mood. The group won't always agree entirely with his views, so he sulks.

Mature roles

The proposer	Initiates ideas and action. Keeps things moving.
The encourager	Brings others into the discussion. Encourages others to contribute. Emphasizes the value of their suggestions and comments. Stimulates others to greater activity by approval and recognition.

The clarifier	Has the ability to step in when confusion, chaos, and conflict occur. He defines the problem concisely. Points out the issues clearly.
The analyzer	Examines the issues closely. Weighs suggestions carefully. Never accepts anything without first thinking it through.
The explorer	Always moving into new and different areas. Probes relentlessly. Never satisfied with the obvious or the traditional viewpoints.
The mediator	Promotes harmony between members — especially those who have trouble agreeing. Seeks to find conclusions acceptable to all.
The synthesizer	Able to put the pieces together from different ideas and viewpoints.[3]

No doubt you will see some of these roles typified by members of your small group. How you deal with members who play out the immature roles and how you encourage and utilize those who take on the mature ones will be an ongoing challenge. Ask the Spirit of God to give you sensitivity, creativity, and ability as you lead. Pray for wisdom to become your constant, ready resource.

YOUR LEADERSHIP: A SPIRITUAL ENDEAVOR

Before we move on, it is important to remember that beyond understanding and fostering discussion, learning to listen well, developing your skill in fashioning questions, and learning to lead different kinds of people, it is God who supplies the grace and strength that will carry you through the challenges of leadership.

This Leader's Guide has focused so far on you and your best efforts, but in truth you will accomplish absolutely nothing of eternal value unless the Spirit of God takes your faithful efforts and infuses them with His enabling power and grace.

For this reason, we encourage you to prepare and lead in complete humility, dependence, and trust, remembering these critical precepts:

I can do all things through Him who strengthens me. (Philippians 4:13)

"My grace is sufficient for you, for power is perfected in weakness." (2 Corinthians 12:9)

"I am the vine, you are the branches; he who abides in Me and I in him, he bears much fruit, for apart from Me you can do nothing." (John 15:5)

Finally, be strong in the Lord and in the strength of His might. Put on the full armor of God, so that you will be able to stand firm against the schemes of the devil. (Ephesians 6:10-11)

Our prayer for you is that of Paul's prayers for the Ephesians:

That the God of our Lord Jesus Christ, the Father of glory, may give to you a spirit of wisdom and of revelation in the knowledge of Him. I pray that the eyes of your heart may be enlightened, so that you will know what is the hope of His calling, what are the riches of the glory of His inheritance in the saints, and what is the surpassing greatness of His power toward us who believe. These are in accordance with the working of the strength of His might. . . . [And] that He would grant you, according to the riches of His glory, to be strengthened with power through His Spirit in the inner man, so that Christ may dwell in your hearts through faith; and that you, being rooted and grounded in love, may be able to comprehend with all the saints what is the breadth and length and height and depth, and to know the love of Christ which surpasses knowledge, that you may be filled up to all the fullness of God. Now to Him who is able to do far more abundantly beyond all that we ask or think, according to the power that works within us, to Him be the glory in the church and in Christ Jesus to all generations forever and ever. Amen. (Ephesians 1:17-19; 3:16-21)

APPENDIX A

THE EFFECTIVE DISCUSSION LEADER: A WORTHY GOAL

This section presents a model for the effective discussion leader (EDL). You may not demonstrate every characteristic listed, nor do you need to. Some of these things you will do very well; others you will do okay; still others may be a weak area for you. That is just fine. Consider this list simply an ideal to aim for. Our hope is that it will motivate you to grow as a small-group leader by revealing your areas of strength and highlighting your areas of weakness for which you may need help. God never said He could use only perfect people in ministry. In fact, your limitations in one or more of these areas may allow for others in the group to come alongside and complement you by contributing their strengths.

You may choose to use this list with a group of leaders to discuss your common ministries and responsibilities and share with each other challenges and successes you've experienced as leaders. Hearing others' thoughts about each of these characteristics might encourage you as you continue to grow.

What key characteristics make an effective discussion leader?

1. EDLs have a good grasp of the material to be discussed.

   - They have studied the material in advance.
   - They have a clear purpose for the meeting.
   - They have an introduction planned.
   - They have questions planned.
   - They have a tentative conclusion in mind.
   - They have examined their own life in relation to the truth of the study.
   - They seek to be diligent workers who accurately handle the word of truth (see 2 Timothy 2:15).

2. EDLs are skilled in organizing group thinking.

   - They know how to use questions.

- They can detect tangents and gently but firmly bring the discussion back on track.

3. EDLs are open-minded.

  - They express judgments in a conditional way.
  - They encourage consideration of all points of view.
  - They encourage open-mindedness on the part of all the members.
  - They are able to handle incorrect answers by inviting further questioning or discussion.

4. EDLs are active participants.

  - They talk frequently yet not excessively.
  - They are not defensive or sensitive to disagreement or criticism.

5. EDLs are facilitators.

  - They do not give dictatorial directions.
  - They encourage participation by all.
  - They encourage interaction among all members.
  - They are able to manage members who tend to dominate discussion.
  - They are able to stimulate and involve shy or reticent members in nonthreatening ways.

6. EDLs speak well.

  - They speak clearly.
  - They speak in a concise, pertinent way.
  - They are not tactless, chattering, offensive speakers.

7. EDLs have respect for and sensitivity to others.

  - They are empathetic.
  - They do not attack others.
  - They do not cause others to "lose face."
  - They are aware of how others are reacting.
  - They are patient.

8. EDLs are self-controlled.

  - They can remain impartial when necessary.

- They can express their feelings in a direct, yet nonaccusatory manner.

9. EDLs can assume different roles.
   - They can give encouragement.
   - They can give direction when necessary.
   - They can insert humor to break the tension when appropriate.
   - They can lead the group in prayer to seek wisdom.
   - They can give personal attention to needy members.

10. EDLs give credit to the group and its members.
    - They praise the group for insights and progress.
    - They stress teamwork.
    - They make all the members feel important.
    - They value others as their equals.
    - They "do nothing from selfishness or empty conceit" but regard others as more important than themselves (Philippians 2:3).

11. EDLs are authentically transparent.
    - They share personal illustrations.
    - They share personal weaknesses, frustrations, pressures, and failures without seeking undue personal attention.
    - They share personal feelings.
    - They share personal requests.
    - They plan ahead so all this can be done with taste and genuineness.

12. EDLs are enthusiastic.
    - They pour themselves into the subject and the discussion of it.
    - They allow the subject to be poured into them by God prior to the discussion.
    - They recognize that genuine enthusiasm is a powerful motivator for others.

13. EDLs are properly critical and evaluative of their leadership.
    - They constantly look for ways to improve.
    - They regularly seek feedback and advice.
    - They consistently evaluate the various aspects of their leadership role.

- They remember that evaluation is not comparing themselves with others but is seeking the Holy Spirit's input on possible improvement.

14. EDLs know that leadership is a spiritual endeavor.

   - They regularly admit to God that apart from Him they can do nothing (see John 15:5).

   - They confidently say "I can do all things" and then humbly add "through Him who strengthens me" (Philippians 4:13).

   - They never forget God's promise that "My grace is sufficient for you" (2 Corinthians 12:9).

APPENDIX B

Suggested Formats for *The Amazing Collection*

The Amazing Collection is intentionally flexible to accommodate a variety of teaching settings and calendars. It is possible to complete the study of all sixty-six books of the Bible in two years by teaching a book a week for thirty-three weeks each year (excluding summers and holidays).

Another option would be to go through the material in three years, teaching a book a week for twenty-two weeks each year, perhaps beginning in September and going through April. Also, for individuals, the program could be completed in approximately fifteen months, studying a book a week for sixty-six consecutive weeks.

There is flexibility in each individual session as well. Sessions might last an hour, in which the group watches the video (forty-five minutes) and allows fifteen minutes for discussion. Or, a 1.5-hour format could include the video, fifteen minutes for refreshments, fifteen for discussion, and fifteen for homework review. If time permits, two-hour sessions could include the video, refreshments, thirty minutes for discussion, and thirty for homework review.

Maybe you'll discover another format that suits your group to a tee. Feel free to use it!

APPENDIX C

SHARING THE GOSPEL

Leaders should be sensitive to the fact that some group members may have an interest in the Bible without having established a personal relationship with its central figure, Jesus Christ.

Sharing the gospel is quite easy for some people and more challenging for others. But if you sense that there are members in your group who would benefit from a clear explanation of salvation, by all means, offer one! There may even be "natural" openings during your course of study (at the end of a book or workbook or during your study of the Gospels or the book of Romans) when the gospel seems to "tell itself." In addition, the vast majority of discussion questions (Old and New Testament) contain a question that points directly to the person of Jesus Christ. These are "teachable moments." Don't miss them.

Several excellent tools exist that can help you walk an unbeliever through the basics of salvation. *The Four Spiritual Laws*, *Steps to Peace with God*, *My Heart — Christ's Home*, and *The Roman Road* are just a few. The leaders in your church may be able to provide you with one or more of them.

Although there are many excellent video testimonies throughout *The Amazing Collection*, it may be appropriate at some point to briefly share your own personal testimony with your group or with one or more of its members. It may help to think of your "story" in four parts: your life before Christ, how you came to know and understand your need for forgiveness and reconciliation with God, what Christ did on your behalf on the cross, and how your life is different today having accepted His atoning sacrifice on your behalf. This is your story! Pray for a sensitive heart, the right timing, and the right words to share it when the Holy Spirit leads you to do so.

It is our prayer that no one would complete *The Amazing Collection* without a personal, saving knowledge of our Savior, the Lord Jesus Christ.